# Felpham Beach

## By Derrick Brewerton
### Emeritus Professor
### University of London

## Dedicated to all members of the
## Felpham Sea Defence Committee

## Available at Felpham shops
## or
## www.pchelpwebshop.co.uk/books

© Derrick Brewerton
'Felpham Beach'
First published 2011

Published by Beach Publishers
21 Davenport Road,
Felpham, PO22 7JR.


Printed by
Printondemand.worldwide


ISBN 978-0-9568991-0-1


A CIP catalogue record for this book
is available from the British Library.
It is also published in the catalogues of
the Oxford Bodleian Library,
the Cambridge University Library,
the National Library of Scotland,
the Dublin Library of Trinity College
and the National Library of Wales.

**All profits will go to the
Royal National Lifeboat Institution**

**Also by Derrick Brewerton:**
'All About Arthritis'
Harvard University Press

## Acknowledgements

I am particularly grateful to every member of the Felpham Sea Defence Committee for their help and for sharing their knowledge.

I am also grateful to many individuals, particularly Leslie Garrett, Sheila Gould, Keith Hellyer and Heather Howell. I had endless advice from many librarians at: the Bognor Regis Library, the British Library, the libraries at the Geological Society of London, Imperial War Museum and Imperial College, and at the University College of London Science Library. Many thanks are due to Frances Lansley and Clare Snoad of the West Sussex Record Office, Martin Hayes of the West Sussex Library Service, and Jennifer Austin of the Bognor Regis Museum. Dr Dominc Fontana of Portsmouth University kindly supplied a high resolution copy of the Cowdray Engraving.

During the period leading to the Coastal Defence Works at Felpham in 1999, I learned from many experts at the Ministry of Agriculture, Fisheries and Food, the Environment Agency, Arun District Council, Portsmouth University, Southampton University, Hydraulics Research, Posford and Duvivier, Robert West, Mouchel, Mackley, English Nature, and the Campaign to Protect Rural England.

# Contents

# Illustrations

# Preface

The stimulus to write this book came in an unusual way. In 1992 Felpham residents were surprised to learn that their District Authority had employed consultant engineers to devise several schemes for constructing new coastal defences. And, in the opinion of the residents, any one of them would have destroyed the beach that they loved. Their immediate response was to set up the Felpham Sea Defence Committee to learn as much as possible about the sea and its local history, and the principles of coastal defence. They would then campaign for the best solution. It was also agreed that I was to be the chairman.

In coastal defence 'one man's defence is the next man's disaster' so the committee deliberately recruited representatives from almost all of the districts between Selsey, a few miles to the west, and Littlehampton to the east. Purposely, we chose enthusiasts from most of the relevant organisations in the area. Above all, they included professional experts who understood subjects related to coastal defence. The members included: a research engineer specialising in fluid dynamics, a civil engineer who had been involved in the building of the Thames Barrier, a marine biologist, two scientists experienced in research, a quantity surveyor, a former harbourmaster/ship's pilot at Littlehampton, a subaqua diver/archaeologist/ geologist with unrivalled experience of our coastline, a coastal defence contractor, an estate agent, a few politicians, sailors, and a banker.

This book is dedicated to every member of the Felpham Sea Defence Committee, all of whom were incredibly keen and knowledgeable. They attended nearly 50 meetings between 1992 and 1999, at which they analysed, debated and rejected ten Options for coastal defence at Felpham, as well organising publicity, fund-raising and other activities.

As I was chairman, ten years later, in 2009 and 2010, I still had a filing cabinet bulging with information that was not generally known to the public. So I decided to put everything together and weave it into a book. I also selected additional material to provide continuity.

The result is not a history book, for I am not a historian. It is a collection of tales, facts, pictures, maps and other information chosen to interest readers and placed in chronological order. In effect it is the story of the South Coast through the ages from the perspective of Felpham Beach.

A previous booklet, called "A History of Felpham Beach", was informal and was simply circulated among local residents. As it proved popular, I decided to write a book and produce it with a more formal layout.

In gratitude to the local lifeboat services, this book is to be sold with all profits to benefit the Royal National Lifeboat Institution.

The author with some of the men who improved our coastal defences in 1999. (With permission from the Portsmouth Publishing and Printing Ltd).

# 𝕱𝖊𝖑𝖕𝖍𝖆𝖒 𝕭𝖊𝖆𝖈𝖍

When writing about Britain's past it is wise to concentrate on one aspect: perhaps a particular period or, as in this book, the viewpoint of Felpham, an unspoilt village on the West Sussex coast. The beach is a good example of many village beaches in Britain, and to a lesser extent throughout the world. It has sand castles, cricket matches, sailing races, swimmers, walkers and ice cream, with a mile-long stretch of sandy shoreline. At the top of the beach are shingle to take the energy from stormy waves and a seawall, while at low tide there are rocks and rock pools to delight the children.

Adjoining the beach is Felpham village, which is next to Butlin's holiday resort and to Bognor Regis. Along the coast are Selsey and Portsmouth to the west, and Littlehampton to the east. On clear days we can see the Isle of Wight beyond Selsey and vessels of all sizes entering and leaving the East Solent. Furthermore, those local residents who sail regard the Solent as part of their home territory. In consequence, I have referred to several important moments in the history of our neighbourhood, including the arrival of the Spanish Armada and the sinking of the Mary Rose.

There are few things better than ambling along a quiet sandy beach, observing the plants and wild life, the children at play and the wavelets lapping on the shore. Or perhaps it is more pleasant to steer a small boat with the sails filled by a strong breeze, or to look out to sea, mug of tea in hand, dreaming of the past. This book suggests several possibilities for those dreams. For instance, how was the beach created?

Figure 1
An international regatta at Felpham.

## Changing coastline.

Today we are liable to think of our shoreline as being fixed. We are horrified if a single house anywhere falls into the sea, or if coastal defence experts advise turning a square mile of vulnerable land into a marsh suitable for wading birds. So it is salutary to remember the immense changes that occurred to our shoreline thousands or millions of years ago. What happened then still has major consequences.

The coast of Britain has changed repeatedly during the last two million years. In West Sussex the sea was so high at some periods that virtually everything from Portsmouth to Worthing and back to Chichester and Arundel was under the sea. In marked contrast, the sea was sometimes very much lower than today.

## Megaflood

Half a million years ago Britain was connected to mainland Europe by the Weald-Artois Ridge, which acted as a dam across the Dover Strait. According to recent research by scientists at Bedford College and Imperial College, a megalake formed in the North Sea fed by the Thames, the Rhine and glacial water from an ice sheet to the north (Figure 2). Between 200,000 and 450,000 years ago this megalake burst through the Dover Strait with immense force and a flow rate of water ten times that of the Mississippi River. Thus the English Channel was born. The consequent megaflood carved out valleys in the seabed as much as six miles wide and 165 feet deep. Later on the sea level was much lower but the essential contours of the seabed caused by the megaflood remained.

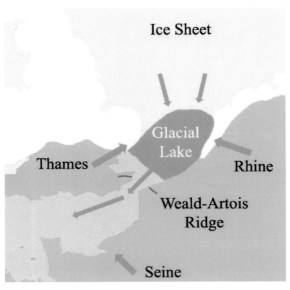

**Figure 2**
**The megalake (after Gupta and Collier).**

## Ice ages

During the ice ages, the climate fluctuated between warm and very cold, with the average temperature changing by as much as 5°C. The cold periods usually lasted for 80,000 to 100,000 years, whilst the intervening warmer intervals lasted only about 10,000 years. The last ice age started 70,000 years ago and was particularly cold from 22,000 to 14,500 years ago, when the North Polar Ice Cap expanded so far south that Northern Europe and Canada were covered by ice thousands of feet deep. In Britain these glaciers reached as far south as Wales and the northern rim of the Thames Valley. South of that area the average temperature was −8° Centigrade and the climate was so dry that the trees died and gave way to tundra.

At the height of the last ice age, 18,000 years ago, the sea level was a remarkable 430 feet lower than today. In consequence, Ireland and the Isle of Wight were joined to the mainland and Britain was physically connected to the Continent of Europe and to Scandinavia: the whole of Britain was simply a peninsula of a continent that included Europe and Asia.

When the last ice age finished, 14,500 years ago, the climate was warmer and more tropical than today, but this proved to be a false dawn for there was a further cold period lasting 1,300 years, until the weather became more reliable 11,500 years ago.

## After the ice ages

When the ice ages ended and the glaciers receded, the sea rose by as much as 3 feet a century at first due to the addition of the melted ice. About 10,000 years ago, as the sea rose the mainland of Britain was separated from Ireland. At that time the English Channel had become little more than an extension of the River Seine (Figure 3) and a hunter/gatherer living at Felpham had to walk 20-mile south to the shore to catch sea bass and salmon.

By 6,000 BC, although the sea had risen almost 250 feet, the shoreline around all of Britain was still an average 20 miles further out than now. At 4,000 BC the rapid rise ended and from 1,000 BC until 1,800 AD it continued at less than an inch a century.

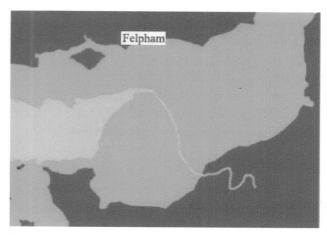

**Figure 3**
**English Channel after the ice ages.**

The Anglo-Germanic Plain (in what is now the North Sea) was a coniferous forest almost 80,000 square miles in area. Then it was covered by the sea about 6,000 BC. Instead of a forest the present-day Dogger Bank between Britain and Denmark is now 165 feet below sea level.

At the same time, the Solent River separated the Isle of Wight from the mainland (Figure 4). Starting at the present Poole Harbour, it flowed eastwards, received a major tributary from Southampton Water and then entered the English Channel opposite Felpham.

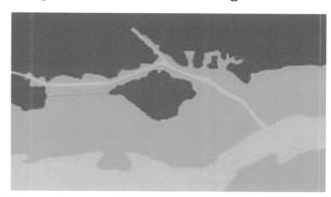

**Figure 4**
**The formation of the Solent River.**

Most of the sea rise had taken place by 3,000 years ago. By then the sea was only seven feet lower than today, but, because the seabed at Felpham was shallow, the seashore was still two miles south of its present position.

During the 20th century, the rate of sea rise is reported to have increased to eight inches a century. It is now over one foot a century, and it is predicted to be over three feet during the coming century – due to the carbon dioxide already present in the atmosphere. [Sadly, the latest evidence from Antarctica suggests that the sea rise this century may be even faster - up to five feet a century - a potential disaster].

In addition to the sea, there is a surprising additional factor: the land in southern England is slowly sinking, causing 'apparent sea rise'.

**Apparent sea rise.**
During the last ice age the north and west of Britain were compressed by glaciers, while the south-east was not. As a result they are still recovering their former heights – very slowly. The north and west of Britain, including Scotland, Ireland and Wales, have been rising, and the south and east of England have been sinking. The accepted rate in the south-east is two inches a century. As a result, some archaeological features in the north and west of the country have remained accessible, while others in the south-east of England have been submerged.

Nowadays coastal engineers working in the south-east of England have to plan for both factors – two inches a century for the tilting of the British Isles and over three feet a century for sea rise. If they are wise, they plan for all eventualities in the next 100 years and allow for a future in which the sea rises more rapidly and storms become more frequent and more violent.

## Life in Ancient West Sussex.

Having described the moving stage on which British coastal history was enacted, we can now consider the cast: the flora and the fauna.

In part of modern Felpham Beach, off Outram Road, there is an SSSI (Site of Special Scientific Interest) which must be left intact even during important coastal defence works (Figure 5). The SSSI preserves a part of the sea bed which is about 60 million years old and rich in fossils, including fruits, seeds, leaves, tree stumps, logs six metres long, the skull of a crocodilian, a beetle elytron and some fish remains.

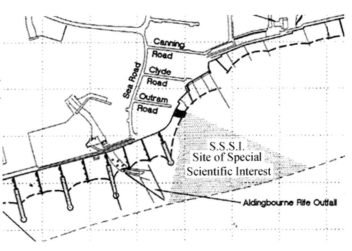

**Figure 5**
**The SSSI shown in a modern plan of Felpham Beach.**

Of course many interesting animals that roamed Britain in the past did not survive the ice ages. A charming story relates how schoolboys discovered bones on a Selsey beach. When members of the staff at the Science Museum in London were contacted these bones proved to be ancient skeletal remains of a rhinoceros. Other animals that did not survive the ice ages included giant deer, several varieties of horse, woolly mammoths, elephants and hippopotamuses.

Judged by stone implements, early forms of mankind lived, had babies, hunted and fished in West Sussex 500,000 years ago. That is before the ice age before last. The Boxgrove Man (discovered close to Chichester) was a hunter/gatherer man who lived 400,000 years ago. However, he belonged to *Homo heidelbergensis*, a branch of mankind that has not survived anywhere. Modern man, *Homo sapiens,* did not appear in Britain until 30,000 years ago.

## Man after the last ice age.

The ice age was so inhospitable that most men and women (perhaps all) and many animals retreated to the south of Europe. For a period after the last ice age, the weather was warmer and a forest flourished on the Anglo-Germanic Plain. This attracted animals, particularly reindeer, some horse, wolf, arctic fox and bear. Men from northern Europe followed about 14,000 years ago, with a few going on to live in Britain.

After the mini ice age, 12,800 to 11,500 years ago, Britain was probably empty again and needed to be repopulated. Consequently, the Anglo-Germanic Plain was a crucial element in the creation of modern Britain because it enabled animals, hunters and their families to walk to Britain from Continental Europe.

The humans who were successful are believed to have been only a few thousand in number. Incredibly, about nine thousand people are thought to have been the founders of England, Scotland, Wales and Ireland, and they are believed to have provided the original gene pools for all of those nations. Obviously, a lot of other people were added later, particularly from Northern Germany, France, Holland , Denmark, Norway and Italy.

## Before the Romans.

The original founders of Britain encountered land that was largely covered by dense forest, with mature trees such as beech and oak - very difficult to clear with the primitive stone tools then available. Consequently, they lived mainly near sea shores and river banks. Felpham would have suited them very well.

At first these people were nomadic hunter/gatherers. Farming and a more settled lifestyle were not introduced until 7,000 years ago. The diet was largely pig, elk, red deer, roe deer, wild boar and wild cattle (aurochs).

The hunters gradually learned to be more settled and make numerous clearings in the forest to grow grass and succulent shrubs that would attract wild animals that they could kill when they pleased.

Hunting included fishing. At first the fishing was mainly with harpoons and arrows, with tips made of flint or reindeer horn. Nets and hooks came later. So it is tempting to imagine ancient people coming to the coast with coracles made of wood and animal skins to spear sea bass and many other varieties of larger fish, much as residents of Felpham today may go out short distances in the sea by canoe to catch sea bass.

Dogs became domesticated at an early stage, and they assisted with the hunting.

## Farming.

Farming came from south-eastern Europe, very slowly, each generation moving on a few miles. It was not until 7,000 years ago that the people of Britain started making larger clearances in the forests so that they could breed animals. Bigger fields for growing crops came much later. Strangely, fishing was largely abandoned as animal meat became more available. With farming came settled homes and a more sophisticated way of life, and their societies divided into different groups, such as farmers, artisans and leaders.

Pottery appeared 5,000 years ago. About 1,000 years later smiths who had been using copper for making implements, learned that, if they added tin from Cornwall to the copper, they made bronze, which was far stronger. Iron came 2,000 years later.

## Tribes.

The people in Britain before the Romans arrived were comprised of many tribes, so that it is difficult to be certain of their names and their allegiances. The most powerful and best known tribes in West Sussex were the Atrebates and the Belgae. The Atrebates (meaning settlers) were a group of tribes with a single dynasty. Their territory extended from West Sussex to Hampshire, and they had Chichester as one of their 'Royal Centres'. The Belgae founded Colchester, St Albans, Winchester (their capital) and probably Portsmouth.

Of local interest to Felpham, the Belgae had an important market on the Selsey Peninsula that exchanged pottery, coins, jewellery, furs, skins and metals, and there was a busy harbour at Selsey (now beneath the sea).

Both the Belgae and the Atrebates had strong links with France and they conducted trade across the English Channel. So the sea was busy with small boats plying around the coast and crossing to the Continent, both for commerce and for social visits.

In the centuries before the Roman invasion of Britain, the Roman Empire expanded on the Continent and many Belgae were displaced from the modern-day northern France and Belgium. Many of them settled in the region of Portsmouth and Winchester, with Cogidumnus as their ruler in West Sussex.

## Julius Caesar.

By 100 BC the British people were used to struggles between tribes and migration from the Continent, but they were not prepared for a Roman military invasion. Everyone learns about Julius Caesar and 55 BC, although in fact it was only a preliminary skirmish during which Caesar set up a camp at Walmer, in Kent. His motives for coming are not clear.

Caesar's hundred ships were probably rowing biremes or triremes, both entirely unsuitable for a Channel crossing (Figure 6). However, they were successful in calm weather because there were no English ships to oppose them. The serious problems began inshore, as the Roman ships were too big to approach the beach and the soldiers were forced to jump into deep water and wade ashore while they were being attacked vigorously by the British warriors. It seems strange to English people, but Caesar, who lived in Italy where the tides are very small, did not allow for a 'spring tide' (when the force of the sun and the moon are in the same direction and produce exceptionally low and high tides). Unwisely, he beached his ships at low tide and they were severely damaged during a spring high tide. As a result, many were wrecked or rendered unseaworthy, necessitating rapid repairs and an early return to France. Caesar learned another lesson: the Britons were superb in the use of chariots – a form of warfare the Romans had not previously encountered.

Caesar came again the following year, a wiser man and better equipped. He prepared for the largest military landing anywhere before the D-day landings in 1944: 800 ships, 5 legions and 2,000 cavalry. As everyone knows, he was more successful the second time, but it was essentially only an exploration, and he soon departed, leaving the Britons and their rulers to continue almost as if nothing had happened.

**Figure 6**
**A Roman rowing bireme.**

## Roman shoreline.

Although the sea continued to roll in while the early Britons were becoming established, in Roman times the shoreline opposite Felpham was still 1.5 miles south of today's coast (Figure 7). That early Roman shoreline was well protected by large shingle banks bound together by sabellaria (worms that live in tubes of sand or fine gravel, which may be built into reefs).

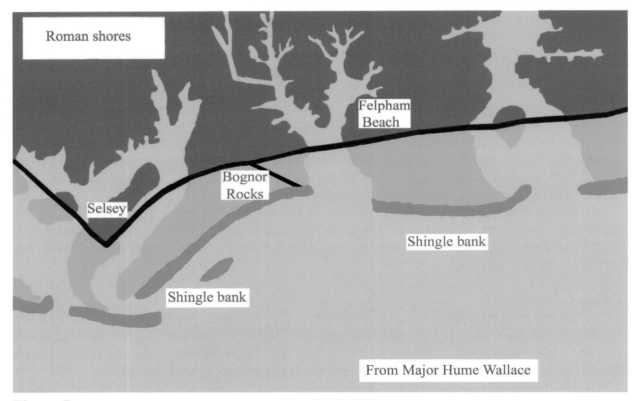

**Figure 7**
Roman shoreline. The present coast is marked in blue. The shoreline in Roman times (2,750 yards further south) is marked in purple. The land that has since been lost to the sea is pale green. Note the massive inland waterways, with the centre one passing through what is now Felpham. (With thanks to the late Hume Wallace).

These shingle banks stood over 2 metres above the highest tides in Roman times. [Hume Wallace reports that the remnants of the protective shingle banks are still present, well below the present sea level]. Some of the land between the Roman and present shorelines, in what we now consider to be far out to sea, was cultivated farm land.

In that time West Sussex had several large inland waterways. The centre one in Figure 7 passed through Felpham village and must have provided an excellent inland beach for fishing. That waterway is now reduced to a small river (the 'Rife').

## Emperor Claudius I.

After Julius Caesar's two landings in 55 and 54 BC, the Britons maintained helpful diplomatic and trade links with Rome. After almost a century, the disabled Emperor Claudius authorised an invasion and, incidentally, reinstated the current king of the Atrebates. The initial force included four legions, consisting of 2,000 men and an equivalent number of auxiliaries. Historians disagree where they landed: it was probably in East Kent but it might have been not far from Chichester. Later, Claudius followed to great acclaim, bringing with him elephants and heavy armaments.

**Figure 8**
**Medusa: Roman mosaic at Bignor,**

The Romans remained in Britain until about 410 AD, leaving behind three famous monuments within a short distance of Felpham: the mosaics at Bignor Roman Villa (Figure 8) and at Fishbourne Palace, and various fascinating historical structures at Selsey, now under the sea.

## A vulnerable coast.

England was subjected to repeated invasion even before the Romans left. In 367 AD the Picts in Scotland and the Saxons in Northern Europe combined to attack England and destroyed villages at will. Consequently, when the Romans left England the people were virtually defenceless. From then until modern times, the South Coast has been attacked repeatedly and Felpham has been at the centre of this activity.

Some immigration was relatively peaceful, while some was highly destructive. Jutes, Angles and Saxons came in large numbers between 300 and 500 AD. In 477 AD a Saxon group landed near Selsey and beat off the defending Britons. They then settled on the Selsey Peninsula.

A further Saxon group conquered the Isle of Wight in 534 AD. As a result, Hampshire and the Isle of Wight became a Jutish kingdom ruled by King Stuf (from Denmark). In 661 AD the Jutes were displaced by Wulfhere of Mercia and forcibly converted to Christianity at sword point! From 772 AD Sussex was a dependency of Mercia until 825 AD, when Egbert of Wessex defeated the Mercians. After that the people happily reverted to paganism.

## Saint Wilfrid.

In 681 AD Wilfrid (later Saint Wilfrid) was shipwrecked on the Sussex coast, where the inhabitants were still pagan. Afterwards, when he was banished from Northumberland, he found refuge on the Selsey Peninsula. With the support of King Aethelwaelth of the South Saxons, he preached the Christian Faith and founded a church/cathedral near the entrance to Pagham Harbour. The cathedral remained the centre of religious activity in the region for almost 400 years, when the Normans decided that all cathedrals should be moved from rural to town sites.

## Vikings.

It is well known that the Vikings occupied the Orkneys, Ireland and much of North-East England, but most of us are less familiar with the repeated attacks on the South Coast from 789 AD onwards or the attempted invasion of Wessex by land in 871 AD. King Alfred (of the burnt cakes), after triumphs and disasters in battles against the Danish Great Army, eventually settled for a compromise. Everything north-east of a dividing line from London to Liverpool was subject to Danelaw, while everything south-west was Saxon England.

In 887 AD six Danish longships came through the English Channel intending to invade and loot the coast of the Isle of Wight. In response, King Alfred dispatched nine of his own longships, which found three Danish ships beached in an estuary of the Isle of Wight and three more on guard. As a result of the ensuing battle, 120 Danes and 62 Saxons were killed. In a peculiar encounter Alfred's boats proved to be too big

**Figure 9**

and all of them grounded on the ebb tide, allowing two Danish ships to escape. They reached the Sussex Coast, where the crews were captured (presumably near Selsey).

After Alfred had died and been replaced by his brother, Ethelred the Unready (975 to 1014 AD), the Danes took over the Isle of Wight and used it as a base for attacking Southern England Their forays were particularly aggressive and included burning down many wooden village churches.

## William the Conqueror.

Against that complicated background, in 1064 William collected together an invasion force of 600 ships and 7,000 men, while King Harold assembled a large army and a fleet of ships in the Channel. Unfortunately for Harold, once everything seemed ready William delayed his invasion for several months, either by accident or design. At harvest time in September 1066, Harold was forced to disband his demoralised army and move his ships to London. Then, to make matters worse, a contender for the throne landed near York just before William sailed from France. With Harold and his much depleted army up north and his fleet in the Thames, William had an uncontested Channel crossing and two weeks

**Figure 10**
**One of William's ships.**

in which to prepare his defences at Hastings - at the end of a peninsula flanked on both sides by impassable marshes. The prolonged battle was one-sided: William had cavalry, infantry and many archers, while Harold had only foot soldiers and a few archers.

Every pupil knows the outcome. Both Caesar and William were successful because the English had no navy in the Channel.

## Arundel Castle and Chichester Cathedral.

Immediately after his successful invasion, William gave most of West Sussex to Earl Roger of Montgomery, who founded Arundel Castle in 1,067. The area around Bramber Castle was given to William de Braose. A little later, Saint Wilfrid's Cathedral in Selsey was moved to Chichester, where it was founded in 1075.

**Felpham Inland Waterway.**

The sea continued to roll in after Roman times. As a result, the inland waterways in West Sussex enlarged and flooded more land, so that the waterway at Felpham was almost 800 yards wide. In today's terms that is from Gloucester Road to Sea Road. Further inland the tidal waterway had increased to almost 3.5 square miles in area, extending as far as Bilsham, Colworth, Shripney and Aldingbourne. This waterway had a considerable influence on the history of Felpham, and it left its footprints for centuries to come (Figure 11).

**Figure 11**
**Modern British Geological Survey. The pale area represents the silt left by the former waterway. (With permission of the National Environment Research Council).**

**Stone churches.**

The builders of the early churches, such as St Mary's in Felpham, which dates back to 1,100, had to import their stone by sea. Therefore, almost all of those shown in Figure 12 were built within 50 yards of the old waterways. Now, if you walk down the path from St Mary's Church to St Mary's Centre, you are walking down the bank of an old waterway. The Centre and the accompanying car park would have been underwater. In the map you can also see that the churches at Middleton and Cudlow were vulnerable.

**Clay.**

The 1864 Ordnance Survey Map (Figure 13) also shows the waterway, as well as a seam of Woolwich and Reading clay that sweeps diagonally across the north of Bognor Regis and ends at Felpham Beach - at the indentation opposite Clyde Road (Figure 14). It is in this part of Felpham Beach that children and some adults dig for clay to make models and to do pottery. To the west of this seam, the soil base throughout Bognor Regis is London clay.

The explanation for the seam of Woolwich and Reading clay was popularised in 1931 by Edmond Venables, a Bognor geologist (Figures 14 and 15).

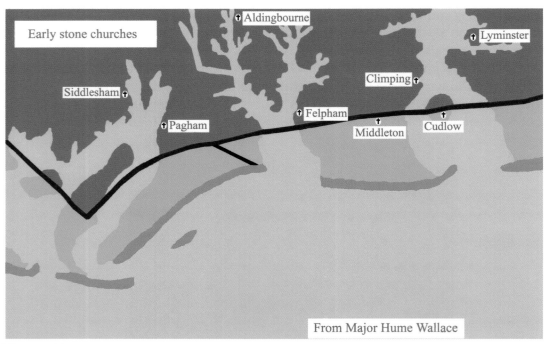

**Figure 12**
Early stone churches. (With thanks to the late Hume Wallace).

**Figure 13**
1864 Ordnance Survey Map. I have tinted the former waterway green and the Woolwich and Reading clay orange. The cliff of London clay is brown, the outlet of the waterway is yellow; and the cliff of Coombe rock is blue.

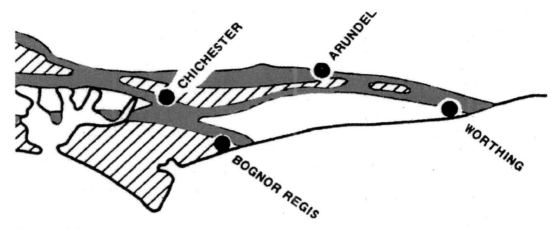

**Figure 14**
**Seam of Woolich and Reading clay in West Sussex (From E. M. Venables).**

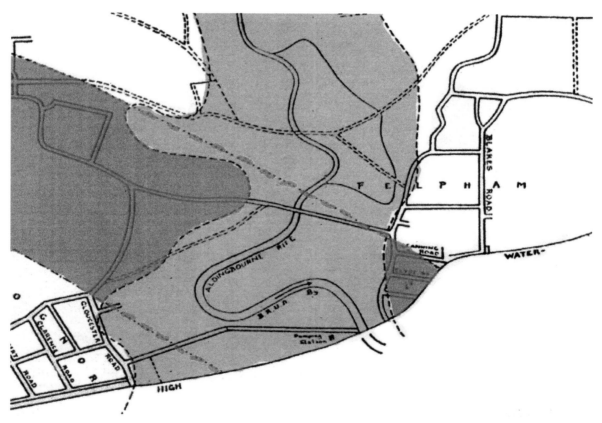

**Figure 15**
  A map by Edmond Venables in 1931. The old waterway, in green, is shown against a background of the roads in his time; the seam of Woolwich and Reading clay is orange/red. (From E.M.Venables).

## Coombe rock and brickearth

Figures 13 and 16 show 'Coombe rock' underlying the eastern part of Felpham beach and the adjacent land. It is a mixture of fine chalk and clay containing flints and some pebbles. Covering the Coombe rock is 'brickearth', which is a clayey loam or silt mixed with rotted vegetation. Brickearth is particularly deep along the coastal plain near Chichester. It does not contain fossils, but in the past it has yielded flints used for man-made implements. Brickearth is what we find in uncultivated fields in our area and it is the basic material in our gardens.

## Shallow cliffs

We have already seen that the underlying composition of our shallow cliffs varies: London clay in Bognor, Reading and Woolwich clay in the indentation, and Coombe rock to the east. Figure 16 is a cross-section of the eastern part of Felpham Beach, illustrating the Coombe rock, brickearth, shingle, sand, and rocks in the sea.

**Figure 16**
**A lateral view of the eastern part of Felpham Beach in cross-section. Coombe rock is green; brickearth is brown; shingle is orange; sand is yellow; rocks in the sea are blue.**

## Inundation.

In the 13th and 14th centuries the shingle banks of Roman times were overtopped and the shingle gradually rolled towards the present shoreline. This mass of shingle blocked the Felpham waterway and made Pagham harbour virtually unusable. Several farms between the Roman/Saxon and the present shoreline were flooded. Villages called Knoll, Kenleigh (in Nyetimber) and Charlton (between Aldwick and Nyetimber) were surrended to the waves. Pagham Parish Council lost the rent from 2,700 acres of farmland, and between 1291 and 1341 Felpham lost 100 acres of agricultural land. The Pagham Records state that by 1,270 the people of Shripney were clearing ditches in the large area of land recently reclaimed from the sea, which included half of the land on which Felpham Village now stands.

**Figure 17**
**Early in the 15th century the area of the waterway near the sea was still wetland. Dry land is dark green and reclaimed land is pale green. Arrows point to the earthworks, road, bridge and fishery.**

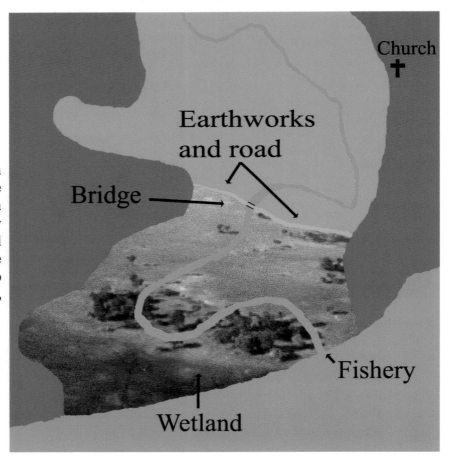

## Early coastal defences.

At the beginning of the 15th century the area of the Felpham waterway nearest the present shoreline was wetland subject to flooding by the sea. The villagers, who were presented with problems remarkably similar to modern-day coastal engineers designing areas of "managed retreat", gave up all attempts to hold the shore as a straight line and abandoned the wetland to wading birds. Instead, they erected a bridge 450 yards inland. By 1436 they had also constructed an earthwork barrier across the waterway at its narrowest point, with a road built on the earthworks, and they had added a new bridge (Figures 17, 18, 37 and 82).

Today, if you drive south out of Felpham Village and turn right onto Upper Bognor Road, you pass over a hump in the road: it is the east end of the earthworks. You can then see the earthworks continuing in people's gardens and traversing the by-pass, Felpham Way, which was built in 1936.

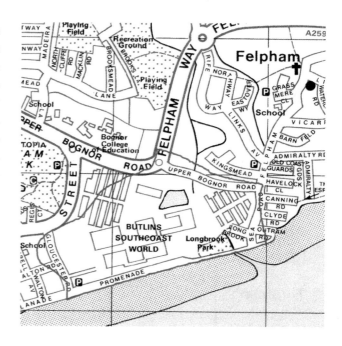

**Figure 18**
A modern map of the same area as Figure 17, with the wetland outlined in red.

## Invaders

Although the Hundred Years' War against France officially lasted from 1337 to 1453, the people on the South Coast lived in fear of French raids for over 500 years. There were also serious wars against the Spanish and the Dutch. In the 1380s, the French had a large fleet which they used to raid the South Coast of England, and they briefly captured the Isle of Wight. During their raids they burned down several South Coast towns, and it was these raids that prompted the building of the famous Bodiam Castle in East Sussex. In 1514 the French burnt Brighton to the ground.

## King Henry VIII.

Against that background, it was King Henry VIII who greatly expanded the British Navy. Then, starting in 1583, he built coastal military defences from Hull in the northeast to Kent, and all along the South Coast round to Wales. For his building material he often used stone from the monasteries that he had dissolved (Figure 19).

## King Francis 1

In July 1545 Francis 1 of France sailed past Felpham into the East Solent with 225 ships and 30,000 soldiers (a larger fleet than the Spanish Armada 43 years later). Once there he landed troops on the Sussex coast and on the Isle of Wight with the aim the aim of using it as a base for attacking Portsmouth. As the French wrote, "having it [the Isle of Wight] under our control, we could then dominate Portsmouth and so put the enemy to extraordinary expense in maintaining a standing army and navy to contain us."

On July 19th the English emerged from Portsmouth – with only 80 ships and 1,200 soldiers. As the next day was calm, the French employed their galleys while the English fleet was motionless. During this engagement the Mary Rose foundered and sank, much to the dismay of Henry, who was watching from Sandown Castle (Figure 20).

As the French troops made no progress, they returned to France the following month having achieved very little.

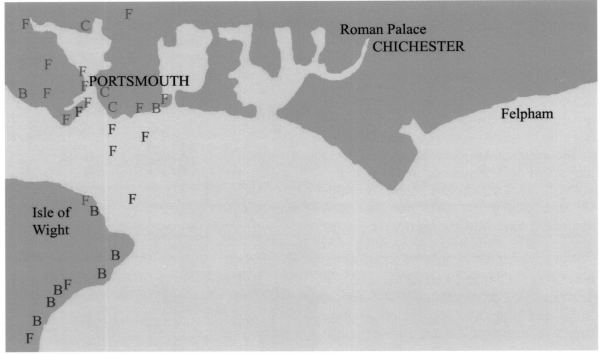

**Figure 19**
A map of defences to protect Portsmouth and the Solent. C = Castle; F = Fort; B = Battery. King Henry's fortifications are in red; subsequent defences (mainly in the 19th century) are in blue.

**Figure 20**
Battle of the Solent. (From the Cowdray Engraving). The British are on the right, the French on the left. The Mary Rose is to the right of the visible gunfire. King Henry (mounted) and Southsea Castle are in the left foreground. Portsmouth town is in the right foreground. Note two men leaving the town with a stretcher. (Thanks to Dr Dominic Fontana. By kind permission of Kesler Kingsley, Portsmouth University).

## Spanish Armada

As a change from the French, the next threat came from the Spanish. However, before the Armada set sail there was ample warning that it was coming. As a consequence, a review of the English defences in 1587 reported that the shore at Felpham, Middleton and Elmer had no cliffs and a shelving beach on to which boats could be run aground. It recommended that earthworks and flanking trenches should be dug to protect the militia, who would be armed with muskets. However, it is doubtful whether this work was carried out. A conflicting report considered that Felpham was safe because of its offshore rocks.

In the same year the English produced their own map (Figures 22 and 23). The shingle banks, so obvious in Roman times, had rolled in and were lying close inshore. The gaps between the shingle permitted small boats to

**Figure 21**
**Spanish Armada. (With permission of the National Maritime Museum).**

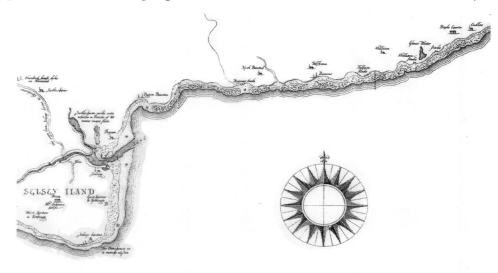

**Figure 22**
**English Armada Map. (With permission of the British Library).**

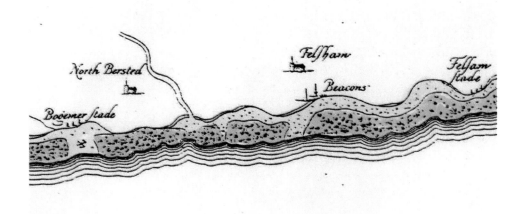

**Figure 23**
**Figure 22 on a larger scale. Sand is yellow; shingle is purple.**

enter and beach on the sand. The absence of beach south of the shingle indicates that our nearshore seabed was already exposed to the sea over 400 years ago.

If you were watching from the low cliff at Felpham on August 3rd 1588, or were among the numerous English spectators following the Armada in small boats, you might have seen the sails of the Spanish ships going about off the Owers, south-east of Selsey.

As the Spanish were in large top-heavy boats, in order to land they would have had to capture a port. So their aim at that stage was to sail up the East Solent and take Southampton. Unfortunately for them, they were outflanked by the smaller, faster, British ships. With wind and tide against him, the Spanish admiral, Medina-Sidonia, had to sail toward the Owers Rocks. However, these rocks were clearly shown on Spanish maps, so his navigators warned him of the danger and he went about just in time. As the sea level was much lower than now, the view of the Owers was described by the Spaniards as, 'The jagged tips of black rocks broke the surface like shark fins'. Having gone about, Medina-Sidonia could find no safe haven on the Sussex or Kent coast. Consequently, he sailed to France, where many of his ships were later destroyed by British fireships.

The beacons to warn of the Armada's arrival are clearly seen in the 1587 map (Figure 23). As Lord Macaulay wrote poetically:
"..the Spaniards saw along each southern Shire,
  Cape beyond Cape in endless range, those twinkling points of fire."

## Dutch Wars.

Next came the four Dutch Wars - in 1652 to 1654, 1665 to 1667, 1672 to 1674 and 1780 to 1784. They were fought for commercial supremacy: there was never any intention by either side to invade the other's land.

These wars were mainly in the North Sea and the English Channel, extending west as far along the South Coast as to engage in the three-day Battle of Portland (in Dorset). The Dutch Wars were also conducted throughout the World, including the Caribbean and India.

After the Great Plague in 1665 and the Great Fire of London in 1666, the Dutch raided the Medway in 1667. This was England's worst naval disaster, in which 15 major ships were destroyed. The Dutch then went on to cause panic by blockading London for a short period.

## Coastal defence.

All the while the residents of Felpham worried about flooding from the rising sea, and a 'Commission for Walls and Ditches for the Rife' was formed in 1422. Before 1454 a sluice was built at the bridge (perhaps a replacement) to prevent flooding further up the Rife. During the fifteenth century the sea repeatedly damaged this bridge and devastated the fishery at the mouth of the Rife, which, incidentally, was owned by the Archbishop of Canterbury (Figure 17). In 1535 a new sluice was built, perhaps on the site of the previous one.

By 1680 much land had been reclaimed by the sea despite a further timber sluice with a double exit built south of the present coastline.

Groynes appeared on maps before 1721, but erosion of the land continued. Newspaper reports in 1820 showed the importance of the inner defences at the earthworks and the sluice (just north of the present Upper Bognor Road). A gale flooded the area now occupied by Butlin's with water over four feet deep near the bridge. And a haystack weighing about 12 tons was washed onto the road.

New defences were constructed by the Sewers Commissioners in the early nineteenth century, only to be partly destroyed by the sea in 1838. Groynes were uprooted and houses by the bridge were flooded. By then the landowners (mainly the Duke of Richmond) had built embankments and groynes to the east of the Rife. After further damage, a new sluice and other works were provided about 1857.

In 1866 a timber sea wall at the mouth of the Rife was badly damaged and was replaced by a concrete wall further inland. In the never-ending fight against the sea, that wall was damaged the following winter and a third wall with new sluices was built still further inland - on the present shoreline. In all, the coast is thought to have receded about 230 yards between 1778 and 1875, with the loss of 3 1/2 acres of Felpham farmland and a cottage. Then, after years of anxiety, the White Windmill finally had to be abandoned in 1879 (Figures 27, 51 and 53).

Work on the Bognor frontage then added to Felpham's problems, following the adage, 'One man's coastal defence is the next man's disaster'. By the end of the nineteenth century more land was eroded, a road near the sluices was destroyed, and several groynes were in disrepair.

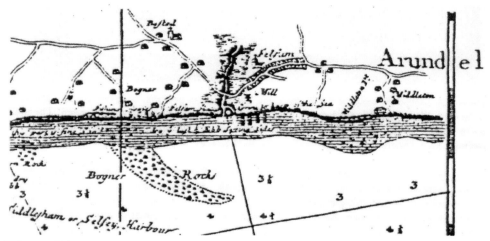

**Figure 24**
**1720 Admiralty Map. (With permission of the British Library).**

**Old maps.**

Whereas modern hydrographers concentrate primarily on shipping lanes and entrances to harbours, between 1700 and 1840 it was important to pay particular attention to the nearshore waters, to aid the navigation of small boats and the prevention of piracy and smuggling.

After the Armada Map in 1587 AD, there were no important maps until the 1720 Admiralty Map by Josiah Avery, 133 years later (Figure 24). This shows the outlines of the old waterway, St. Mary's Church, the Felpham Sluice, the Black Windmill, four groynes and Bognor Rocks. The massive shingle banks from Roman times had disappeared. The 3 1/2 fathoms depth east of Bognor Rocks is equivalent to 8 metres below Ordnance Datum today.

Next is the Yeakell and Gardner map of 1778 AD (Figure 25). This was a superb pioneering undertaking by independent individuals. It shows excellent detail of the land and the main rocks in the sea, but it provides little detail of the shoreline. [I have coloured the old estuary in green]. This map does not copy well, but in the original map you can see the sluice and an apparent reduction to two groynes just to the east of it. The indentation that features in later maps is not shown.

**Smugglers and Pirates.**

Heavy duties on the export of wool were imposed as early as 1274. This resulted in the illicit export of wool late in the thirteenth century, a trade that was particularly common in Sussex and Kent because of the sheep on the downs and the proximity to France. In Felpham, four unmounted coastguards were appointed in 1295, although Riding Officers not until 1699.

Describing smuggling on the Sussex coast, Norman Wymer wrote, "The coast proved a haven for the smugglers who were so active there. Every little inlet from west to east, was a landing ground for contraband of some kind, be it spirits, tobacco, tea or lace: every river or waterway along which to take illicit goods to a safe inland hideout." In fact, Pagham Harbour, Elmer, Climping and Littlehampton provided popular landing sites. Chichester and Arundel

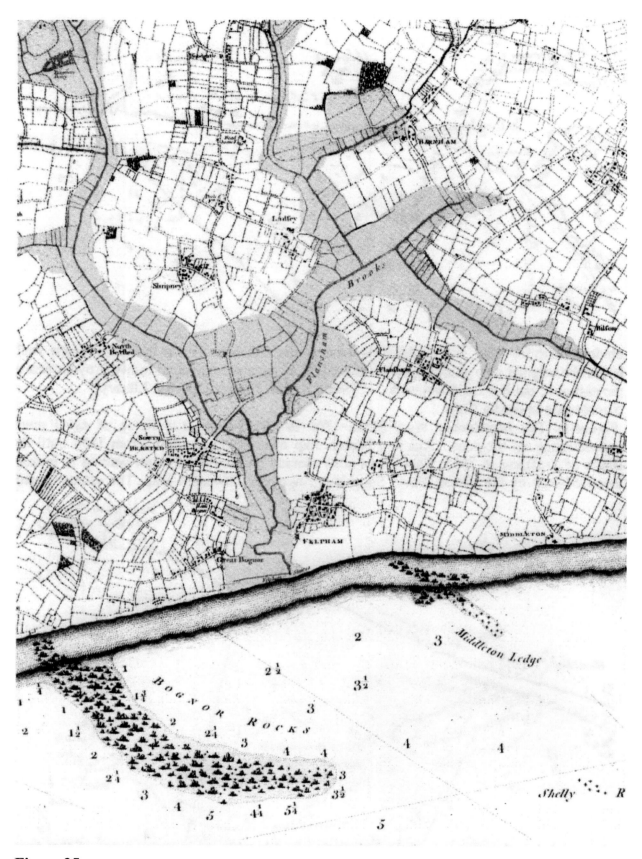

**Figure 25**
   The Yeakell and Gardner Map. (With permission of the British Library). I have tinted the old waterway green.

were among several regular inland staging posts. Kent and Sussex were popular at that stage because they were nearest to both the London market and the continental suppliers.

There is little evidence of smuggling at Felpham before the 18th century. By then the emphasis was on import, particularly of tea, brandy, gin, silk, lace and tobacco. Bringing cargoes ashore presented no problem for the fishermen, and many local residents were drawn into hiding goods.

The French often co-operated with the smugglers and built warehouses on the French Coast where smugglers could select suitable goods. The smugglers then brought the contraband to England in fishing boats or fast cutters. Once in shallow water, the land gangs would unload. If the vessels could not come close inshore, they used 'tub-boats', specially constructed shallow rowing boats. In villages such as Felpham, the local people would hide the goods in outhouses, barns or cellars until they could be moved further inland.

## French raiders and the Seven Years War.

As I have already said, for several centuries the residents of the South Coast continued to live in fear of French raiders, who would plunder, sack and burn whole villages.

A sideline of smuggling was assisting French spies. An early local triumph for the first Felpham Riding Officer was when he arrested two French spies as they were being landed.

The Seven Years War with France officially began in 1756. Soon after, French troops gathered between Dunkirk and Cherbourg and added to the English anxiety. Felpham people were well aware that, if Portsmouth were invaded, troops were likely to land on the empty beaches between Selsey and Felpham in order to attack Portsmouth from the rear. In fact, the advice of a French spy was to land two French army corps between Selsey and Littlehampton. One army was to swing round to attack Portsmouth, while the other would take the North Downs between Guildford and Dorking before going on to London.

To protect this coastline, the English established three 36-pounders east of Selsey and two more at Aldwick. Part of the defence was to remove everything of value to the enemy. Food, cattle, carts and horses were to go inland, and the local people were to be encouraged to leave. If they didn't, the soldiers were to destroy anything useful without hesitation.

After the war, a French spy carrying out reconnaissance in South-East England, described the English as, ".. dull people who are absolutely ignorant of the use of Arms".

From 1783 to 1815 there was constant concern that the French might invade. If they did, they would need to capture a major port, such as Portsmouth or Chatham. If Portsmouth were chosen, West Sussex would have been part of the battleground. During the 1790s the French actually made several unsuccessful attempts to land troops at various sites on British soil.

## Owers Lightship

The Owers Lightship was first operated in 1788. From then on its rotating light was readily visible to anyone standing on Felpham Beach on a clear night. Sadly for us, it was replaced by a small, automatic floating lighthouse in 1973.

## Felpham Windmills.

Two windmills were reported in Felpham as early as 1341, although their sites are not clear. Windmills were prominent features for many years (Figure 29). They appeared on many Admiralty Charts and Ordnance Survey Maps.

A Black Windmill, a post mill with four sweeps, was the only mill in the parish in the 17th and 18th centuries. It was not used after 1896.

The White Windmill was built about 1800. An imposing seven-story, white stone, smock mill, it could generate 27 horse-power and drive four pairs of stones. Very unwisely, it was built with one foot on the beach, as shown in Figures 27 and 51. After years of anxiety, it eventually succumbed to the sea and was demolished in 1879.

## William Blake

Until he was 42, William Blake, the genius, prophet, painter and engraver, was brought up, educated and employed in central London. Then, in 1800, William Hayley offered him regular work at Felpham. Thus Blake and his wife set off on the 17-hour journey from London, involving six changes of carriage. He had never seen the countryside before then.

**Figure 26**
**William Blake (1807) by Thomas Phillips.**

Once in Felpham, Blake rented a cottage for £20 a year, which he described as the 'sweetest spot on earth'. From his bedroom window he could see the 'far-stretching sea, with many a white sail gleaming at sunset'.

It soon became Blake's custom to go down the narrow lane to the sea, where he would step over the shingle and go for walks along the sandy beach. As one result, he did a sketch from the beach at low tide (Figure 27) illustrating the open fields between the beach and his cottage. In the foreground is the newly-built White Mill.

Blake's angels knew what they were about when they sent him to his 'three years slumber beside the ocean'. Prompted by his 'daughters of inspiration' (Figure 28) he worked on his poem 'Milton', which starts with the immensely popular anthem 'Jerusalem'. It is worth comment that, until he left London, he had no personal experience of 'England's green and pleasant land'. Also, the sea in some of Blake's paintings may have been inspired by life at Felpham.

**Figure 27**
**Sketch of Felpham Beach by William Blake (1800 - 1803). Evidently sketched from the beach at low tide, this picture includes, from left to right, the White Windmill, St. Mary's Church, Hayley's Turret, Blake's cottage and bright sunlight on the beach. There are open fields between the beach and both Blake's cottage and Felpham Village.**

**Figure 28**
   Blake drawing (from *Milton*). A 'daughter of inspiration' descends towards Blake at his cottage in Felpham.

**Figure 29**
   Felpham's Black and White Windmills in a 1839 watercolour said to have been sketched on the spot. The sea is on the right. (With permission of the West Sussex County Council Library Service).

## Napoleon Bonaparte

Between 1793 and 1815 Britain and France were actually in a state of war. Invasion seemed particularly threatening in 1798, 1803 and 1805, leading to a state of emergency all along the South Coast. Starting in 1803 Napoleon assembled an army of 110,00 men on the French coast waiting to invade England. Thanks to his spies, he had a detailed map of the entire British coastline (Figure 31). With a flotilla of more than 2,000 boats, including flat-bottomed boats propelled by sail or oars, he was well equipped to land on the open beaches. However, as most of his boats could not tack against the prevailing south-west wind in the Channel, the flotilla would have been decimated in a gale, making invasion in the winter impossible. When he reviewed his flotilla in Boulogne, he ignored the advice of his admirals, like Hitler in the next century. As a result, twenty sloops went aground in a storm, drowning 2,000 men. After that harsh lesson, Napoleon gave up his invasion plans and marched his troops towards Austria. In reality, his plan was never feasible as long as the British Navy controlled the Channel. Also, England had an Army of 160,000 men and a further 500,000 men under arms.

**Figure 30**
**Napoleon. By Jacques Louis-David.**

As everyone knows, because the combined French and Spanish fleet remained a serious threat to British interests, Admiral Nelson decided that it had to be stopped. After pursuing Villeneuve to the West Indies and back, he destroyed the combined fleet at Trafalgar in 1805.

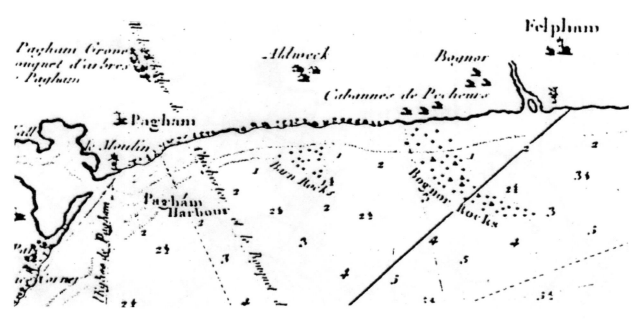

**Figure 31**
  **Napoleon's Invasion Map. Note the old waterway at Felpham, the fishermen's cabins, and the Bognor Rocks. (With permission of the British Library).**

## Admiralty Maps

The Napoleonic Wars (from 1793 to 1815) brought a flurry of British Admiralty maps concentrating on the coast – in 1804, 1807, 1813 and 1816. Good examples are 1807 and particularly 1816, which illustrates the complexity of the observations recorded (see Figures 32 to 34).

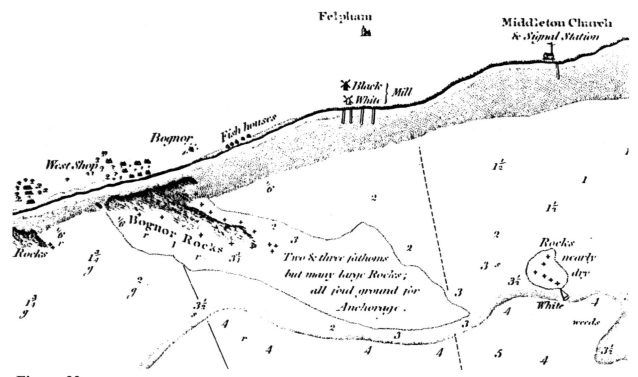

**Figure 32**
**1807 Admiralty Map. (With permission of the British Library).**

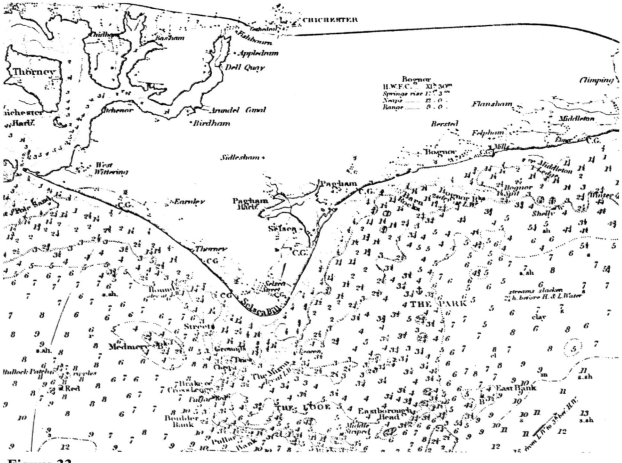

**Figure 33**
**1816 Admiralty Map. (With permission of the British Library).**

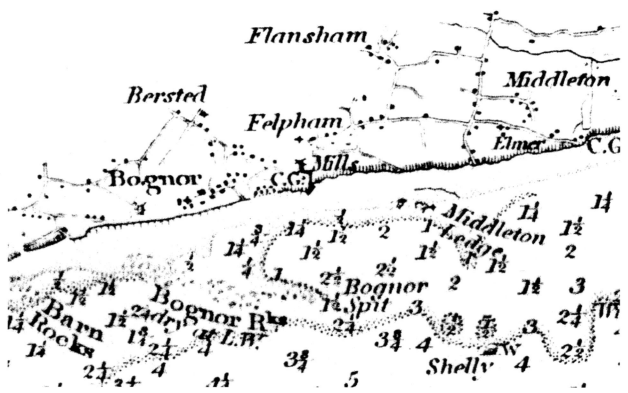

**Figure 34**
**1816 Admiralty Map in greater detail.**

**Figure 35**
**1813 Ordnance Survey Map. (With permission of the British Library).**

## Old Survey Maps

The Army was also busy, although from a different perspective: they were interested in the land, while the Navy concentrated on the sea and inshore waters. Starting in 1792 surveys were conducted by the Royal Military Surveyors and Draughtsmen based in London. The first Ordnance Survey (figure 35), published in 1813, shows the indentation by the White Windmill. The most likely explanation for the indentation is an abrupt change in the geology of the land (where London clay gives way to Woolwich and Reading clay). There are three groynes at Felpham and three more towards Middleton.

The first more detailed map is the Felpham Inclosure Map of 1826, drawn in order to show the ownership of the land (Figure 35). As you can see, most of it belonged to the Duke of Richmond and the Reverend Charles Webber. The Black and White Mills are shown.

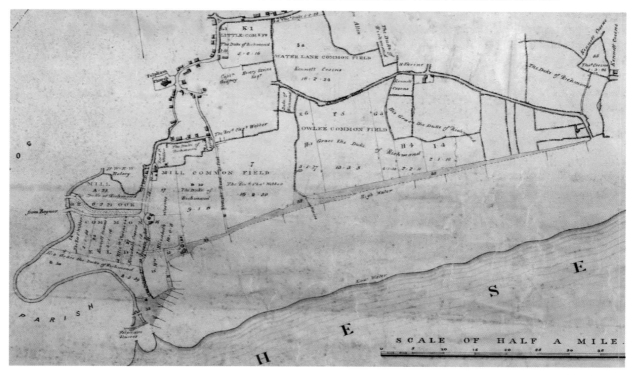

**Figure 36**
**The 1826 Inclosure Map. (With permission of the West Sussex Record Office).**

Next comes the Felpham Tithe Map of 1844. It is difficult to reproduce and contains few new details. The legal requirement for a farmer to pay a tenth of his annual turnover to the established Church had been in existence for over a thousand years. In 1836, due to strong objections to paying to make the clergy rich, a new act was introduced: the obligation was changed to a rent paid by all parishioners. Hence a Tithe Survey was conducted between 1836 and 1850.

The 1864 Ordnance Survey Map was described on page 9 and illustrated in Figure 13.

The 1876 Ordnance Survey (Figure 37) is the first large scale Survey Map by the Army. It illustrates several new features:

1. The waterway that was once 800 yards wide is now a narrow, tortuous river, the 'rife'. Note the tributary close to where the present village is sited and the sluice at the exit to the sea.

2. I have marked in brown the earthworks constructed early in the fifteenth century.

3. The Black and White Mills.

4. The area bought by the Admiralty for the coastguard station, the adjoining coastguard cottages and the boatshed by the White Mill.

5. The Fox Inn, named after one of the coastguard cutters.

6. Blake's cottage.

7. The beach. Note that the Mean Low Tide is almost 300 yards from the low cliff and several groynes have been built longer than today to match the lower tides at that time.

**Figure 37**
**1876 Ordnance Survey Map. (With permission of the West Sussex Record Office).**

## Coastguard Station

Felpham was still only a small community of 600 souls in 1870, mostly engaged in farming. So the addition of a coastguard station was an important factor in the development of the village. It was also a prominent feature of Felpham Beach.

In 1861 the Admiralty bought a field of twelve acres immediately to the west of Blake's Road, extending from the present promenade almost to Vicarage Lane (see Figure 37). To the west of that field there were fifteen cottages for the staff (still in use) and a detached house for the officer. The total population was 46 people.

Near to the sea was a watchhouse and probably an armoury. A boatshed was built next to the White Mill. When that was abandoned in 1879, a new boathouse was built to the east of the end of Blake's Road, with a launching slipway to the sea.

After a while the coastguards adopted fast cutters, and one of them, the 'Fox', gave its name to the inn nearby. Once the Coastguard Service was established, smuggling was soon stamped out.

26

### Prime Minister Palmerston

By 1859 there was mounting concern that Napoleon III of France might invade the South Coast, so the government set up a Royal Commission on the Defence of the United Kingdom. The Commission published papers warning of the vulnerability of Portsmouth Harbour, resulting in a new encircling line of forts to protect it from attack on land, or by sea.

The 'Palmerston Forts' were then built, including the Spithead, Gosport and Portsdown Forts in the Solent (see Figure 19). Two years later the Horse Sands, No Mans Land and St Helen Forts were built.

### Sporting pastimes

On the light side, there were bathing machines at Felpham by 1781, and soon after there were holiday houses to let and opportunities for sailing. There were also boat trips to Selsey Bill and the Ower's Lighthouse. A cricket club was founded at Felpham in 1886, using a field to the west of the rife. Early in the twentieth century tennis and golf were developed. The tennis courts were added in Blake's Road in 1914 and the putting green in 1928 (Figure 97).

### Basic features

Now that we are approaching the twentieth century in our narrative it is time to review some other features of our coastline.

### Incoming tide

We have already seen that the sea was 430 feet below the present level during the last ice age. In contrast, the sea is now rising at an accelerating rate, and the tide is steadily moving up the beach.

To illustrate this change, I have compared the Mean Low Tide on six maps: the Inclusion Map of 1826 and the Ordnance Survey Maps of 1876, 1898, 1932, 1970 and 2010. On each map I have taken the same five sites on the beach and measured the distances from the 'Mean Low Tide' to the position where our sea wall stands at present. I have then calculated the average for each date. The results were: 365, 280, 255, 215, 150 and 110 yards respectively. In other words the Mean Low Tide moved 255 yards up the beach in less than two centuries (Figures 37 and 38). Of course the rate at which the tide comes in will now slow as the beach becomes steeper but accelerate due to the recent rapid increase in sea rise.

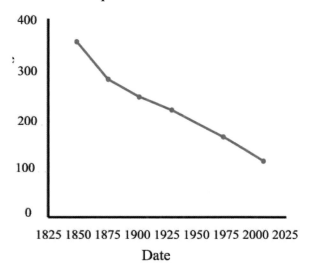

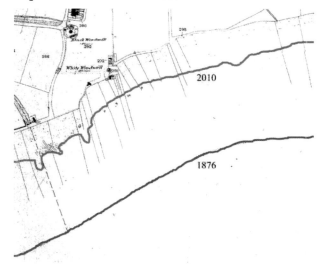

**Figure 38**
This graph shows the average distance in yards that the Mean Low Tide has moved up the beach since 1826.

**Figure 39**
The 1876 Ordnance Survey Map with the Mean Low Tide in blue. The Mean Low Tide in 2010 is superimposed in red.

## Flood risk

There are several factors that determine whether a particular area will be flooded. They include:

1. The level of the land.
2. Whether water can escape.
3. Whether an inland waterway such as Chichester Harbour is a large expanse that narrows in the direction that the wind and waves are moving. Then the water piles up at one end – far more than determined by the calculated levels of land and water alone.

The first factor illustrates why we have spent so much time on the old waterway. If the defences were seriously breached between Gloucester Road and Canning Road, the sea might reclaim its own. Over 3 1/2 square miles of low-lying land would be at risk.

As examples of the second factor, flood water in the middle of Felpham Beach Estate would quickly drain north-westwards towards Limmer Lane, while water in Butlin's or Sea Road could not escape because of the sea wall.

The third factor would not affect Felpham today, but if the hurricane in 1987 had been at high tide instead of low tide, serious flooding in Chichester would have occurred because water would have piled up at the east end of Chichester Harbour. However, problems in Felpham would have been very serious centuries ago. Imagine a southerly gale driving waves up the waterway, or, in more recent centuries, the damage caused by storm waves hitting the banks of the wetland (the marsh at the opening of the former waterway).

## Shingle

Those who live on the South Coast of England often assume that shingle is common. In fact, worldwide it is comparatively rare and we are unusually fortunate to have it. The shingle takes much of the energy out of incoming storm waves, and therefore it is by far the most effective natural coastal defence where there are no cliffs.

It is also commonly assumed that the shingle we see on a particular day is the same as the day before. But shingle washed by the sea is highly mobile: experimental pebbles on an open beach (without breakwaters) have been shown to move 1,000 yards during one high tide in a storm. (From Malcolm Bray, Portsmouth University).

**Figure 40**
**Shingle**

Most shingle at Felpham comes from the seabed at Selsey, and it is carried westward by the prevailing waves coming from the south-west. Some of the pebbles have been conveyed inshore by large seaweed such as kelp. When young, the seaweed attaches itself to stones on the seabed. Then, when the seaweed has grown, it is dragged ashore by currents, pulling even large stones with it. What proportion of pebbles is transported in this way is not known.

The amount of shingle moving along the coast varies from year to year and decade to decade, so our coastal protection varies accordingly. Why, nobody knows.

## Sand

To the disappointment of many children, the sand on Felpham Beach is usually a thin veneer covering a thicker layer of grit - excellent for cricket but poor for building large sandcastles! (Figure 41).

Nobody knows where our sand comes from because it is virtually impossible to do experiments on sand transport. To me the best suggestion is that it comes in the opposite direction to the shingle and by a different mechanism (Figure 42). This theory is that our sand is carried down tributaries of the River Arun from the flat area between Amberley and Pulborough. It may then escape detection in the Arun because it travels in a narrow channel in the middle of the riverbed. Once the sand reaches the sea it is transported westward along the shore by the tidal currents near high tide. Everyone who has swum at Felpham at high tide knows that it is more difficult to swim eastward against the current than westward. By this mechanism the sand travels westward at high tide and is deposited on the beach. Then, when the current is in the opposite direction at low tide, the sand stays put because it is literally high and dry.

Of course, there are many other factors, such as storm waves, tides, other tidal currents, seabed friction, natural rocks and winds. In the end, however, the movement westwards wins out, and eventually sand is deposited on the massive sand banks of the East Solent.

Some years we enjoy plenty of sand, other years there is much less. Nobody knows why. Often it is the opposite to the accumulation of shingle. Perhaps storms bring shingle and at the same time wash sand out to sea.

**Figure 41**
**Digging sand at Felpham.**

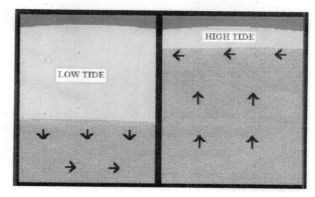

**Figure 42**
**A theory to explain sand movement.**

**Felpham Rocks**

The rocks on our beach (Figure 43) start 50 to 100 yards from the sea wall and extend about 2,700 yards out to sea.

In 1835 Sir Woodbine Parish described our rocks to the Geological Society in London:

" *about a mile to the east of Bognor, and in front of the village of Felpham, chalk is exposed for a considerable distance, cropping out of the sands between the high and low water and at low water it may be traced for upwards of a mile in the direction of Middleton.* "

Sir Woodbine also produced a long list of fossils that could be found in our rocks.

In fact our offshore rock is at the end of a series of chalk rocks that extends from Littlehampton to Felpham. Our chalk rock is the toughest - *Belemnitella mucronata*. Although some of these rocks are over three feet above beach level, they are not shown in the latest Admiralty Chart.

Opposite the middle of Davenport Road there is a geological fault resulting in a break in the rocks about 100 yards wide, making it a favourite place for swimming or launching small boats. Figure 44 is an aerial photograph that shows the geological fault.

An important feature of these chalk rocks is that they harden in salt water and soften gradually and finally disappear in fresh water. Consequently, rocks of this type near a river outlet may soften and then vanish, leaving their contents, such as flints, on the seabed.

**Figure 43**
**Felpham rocks.**

**Figure 44**
**Geological fault.**

## Seabed

In some areas of the seabed it is comprised of flints and sand (Figure 45). In Figure 46 I have produced a composite map on the basis of information from fishermen, divers, yachtsmen, windsurfers and aeronautical photographs. You can see the Felpham, Middleton, Bognor and Shelly Rocks, some named inshore rocks and the geological fault. Superimposed are the soundings from the latest Admiralty Chart.

The yellow area is the site of the old estuary, with a surface of sand and stones. This area is deeper than the purple area to the east, but not as deep as it was: 7 to 8 metres below Ordnance Datum two or three centuries ago, compared with 1.6 to 3 metres today. So the

**Figure 45**
**Flints on the seabed.**

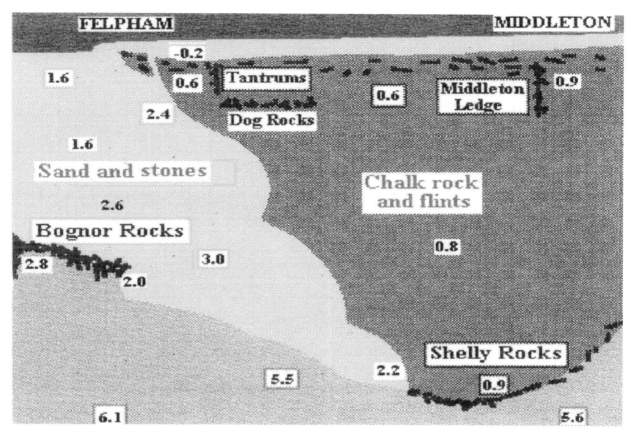

**Figure 46**
Map of the seabed. Yellow is the old waterway, with a surface of sand and stones. Purple is mainly a mixture of chalk, loose flints and sand, extending 2,750 yards out to the Shelly Rocks. Superimposed are the soundings from the latest Admiralty Chart.

seabed there appears to have risen 4 metres. The depth of this area partly explains why the indentation gets less protection from southerly and south-easterly gales.

The purple area is mainly a mixture of chalk, loose flints and sand - good crab and lobster country. This extends 2,750 yards out to the Shelly Rocks and is well over a square mile in area. Its overall elevation is remarkably uniform, due to a process in the distant past known as 'planation'. It is nowhere more than a metre below Ordnance Datum. At low tide springs we can windsurf out there and get off and walk around - carefully - anywhere in that area.

Due to its very uneven relief, the chalk rock provides spaces in its hollows where sand can move offshore during violent storms and then feed back inshore in calmer times. It is also important that our rough natural rocks slightly reduce the wave attacks on the coast.

It is 700 years since the sea overtopped the Shelly Rocks and began to erode the surface of brickearth. As one might expect in a marine environment, the chalk rock has withstood the action of the sea over at least four centuries remarkably well.

**Seaweed**

Once every few years, seaweed is a serious problem all along the local shores. At the very worst, any time from May to September a stinking, squelching, fly-ridden mess up to three feet deep may cover beaches for weeks at a time. The result is misery for residents and holiday-makers alike (Figure 47).

Rarely, seaweed can also be dangerous. Anaerobic decomposition of the weed when covered by sand can create areas on the shore with the consistency of quicksand, particularly near groynes. Very rarely, highly toxic pools of hydrogen sulphide may form.

The many types of seaweed in our area vary considerably in their growth from year to year and in different seasons of the year. Our main problem is with what fishermen call 'slub', which washes ashore during the summer months and becomes stranded at the top of the beach, where it disintegrates over a few days and gives off hydrogen sulphide - reminiscent of sewage but totally unrelated to it. In contrast, different varieties of seaweed, including *chorda filum, laminaria, fucus vesiculosus* and *sargossum muticum,* reach our beaches mostly in the autumn and winter after they have died off due to lack of light, floated to the surface and have then been carried onto the beaches by storm waves. By a different process, slub usually comes ashore in calm conditions, often when there is an offshore breeze. As the surface water moves offshore, the deeper water comes inshore, bringing the slub with it. Two of the main culprits are *desmerestia aculeata* ('Landlady's wig') which has

**Figure 47**
**Seaweed (slub with flecks of sea lettuce).**

acid vesicles which speed the disintegration of surrounding seaweeds, and *ulva lactuca* ('Sea Lettuce') which is notorious for its production of hydrogen sulphide. Rarely, miserable piles of seaweed remain on our beaches, despite all the efforts to remove them, until they vanish during a storm.

## Groynes (breakwaters)

For costal defence, the main purpose of groynes (Figure 48) is to impede the tidal currents and the action of the waves in order to retain shingle. The authorities regard the fact that groynes also help to retain sand as incidental.

## Fishermen

One of the delights of Felpham Beach in the past was provided by the local fishermen, with their boats, nets, lobster pots, prawn pots and fishing tackle (Figure 49). There was always fresh-caught fish to buy on the seafront: fresh plaice, sole, whiting, herring and mackerel, as well as shell fish, lobsters and prawns. Above all there were the fishermen.

A major tragedy caused widespread grief in 1,900, when two fishermen, William Hellyer and Harry Watkins, were drowned.

**Figure 48**
**Groynes (breakwaters).**

Three men had rowed out in high seas to get lobsters from a 'penner'. On their return journey their boat was overturned by an exceptional wave and two of the three men were lost.

In happier times there were boat trips for the children (Figure 50). In 1940 the 'White Spray', the boat in which many children enjoyed themselves, made the long journey to rescue stranded soldiers of the British Expeditionary Force on the beaches of Dunkirk.

**Figure 49**
  Felpham fishermen. (With permission of the West Sussex Library Service).

**Figure 50**
  Crew of the 'White Spray' with young admirers. (With thanks to Keith Hellyer).

## Housing Development

What is now known as the Snook's Corner Community has been an important neighbourhood close to Felpham Beach. The 1826 Inclosure Map shows a 'Private Road' extending from the Black Mill to the sluice where the rife reaches the sea (Figure 36). This was named Sea Road and laid out in 1840 under the Inclosure Act of 1826. Blake's Road was laid out at the same time. The roads adjoining Sea Road: Canning Road, Clyde Road and Outram Road did not appear in the 1876 Ordnance Survey (Figure 51), but they were already laid out when that area was offered for sale as the Felpham Mill Building Estate in 1884, and they appeared in the Ordnance Survey of 1898 (Figure 52). The houses on the estate were then built piecemeal over the next twenty-five years (Figures 53 to 55).

Early in the twentieth century, cheaper houses were built near the sea. (Figure 54) They stood on stilts to avoid flooding and many of them were made from disused railway carriages.

At the same time, housing spread north and east from the Coastguard Station. It then began in Felpham Beach Estate to the east (Figure 61). Summerley Estate was laid out in 1922.

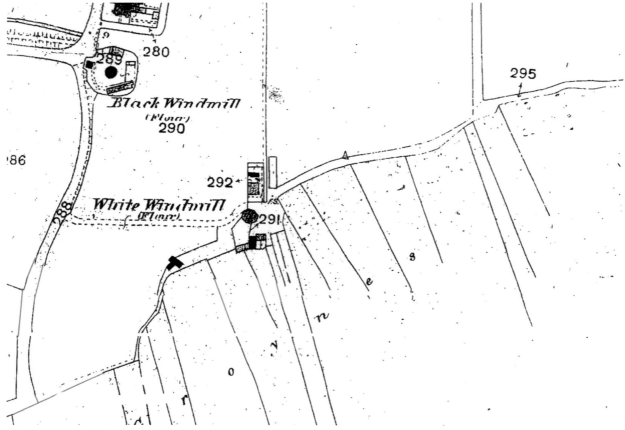

**Figure 51**
**1876 Ordnance Survey. Note the present Sea Road (marked 288) and the two mills (marked 289 and 291). (With permission of the West Sussex Record Office).**

## Loss of property

Considering all the problems that the sea had caused in the past, it is remarkable that the White Mill was built in 1800 in such a vulnerable position (Figures 27, 51 and 53). After years of anxiety, it was eventually abandoned in 1879. Comparison of Figures 50, 51 and 52 shows that, in addition to the mill, land to the east was lost as far as Blake's Road. To make this more obvious, on the 1932 Ordnance Survey (Figure 53) I have drawn a dark blue line where the cliff was shown in 1876 and a red line on the corresponding low wall at the top of the beach in 1932. The intervening lost land is pale blue.

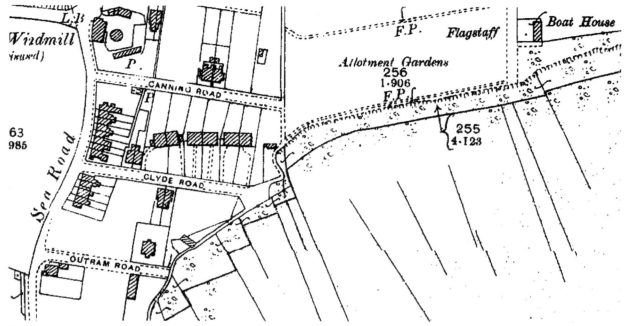

**Figure 52**

1898 Ordnance Survey. The White Mill has been demolished; the new Boat House is shown; part of the Coastguard property has become allotments; Sea Road, Canning Road; Clyde Road and Outram Road have been developed. (With permission of the West Sussex Record Office).

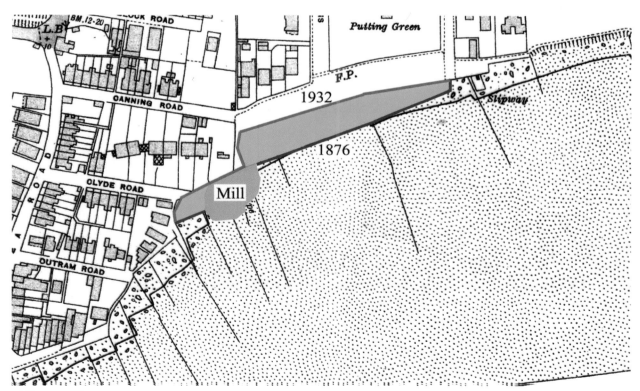

**Figure 53**

1932 Ordnance Survey. The Sea Road Community has developed. The allotments have given way to houses and a putting green. To show where the White Mill and its surrounding buildings once stood, their site is marked in brown; and to show the land that has been lost, the 1876 cliff is shown in dark blue and the 1932 cliff in red. The intervening land that was lost is pale blue.

## Twentieth century

For the period 1900 to 1939 I am indebted to the West Sussex County Council Library Service and the West Sussex Past Picture website, 'www.westsussexpast.org.uk', which are goldmines of old pictures.

**Figure 54**
Felpham Beach in 1914. (With permission of the West Sussex Library Service).

**Figure 55**
Beach carriages at the end of Sea Road in 1905. There is a vulnerable wall in the foreground and in the background on the far side of the promenade. (With permission of the West Sussex County Council Library Service).

**Figure 56**
  Felpham Beach in 1910. The man in the foreground leaning on a bicycle has one foot on a low sea wall. Near him there is a remarkable absence of groynes. (With permission of the West Sussex Library Service).

**Figure 57**
  Felpham Beach in 1914. This shows the indentation and several tall groynes, some supported by timber props. (With permission of the West Sussex Library Service).

**Figure 58**

Felpham Beach in 1929. This view is well to the east of the others – beyond the low sea wall. The groynes are in such poor repair as to be almost useless. Instead of a wall, there is a simple slope leading to beach huts, which apparently stand on the beach. Overall, there is remarkably little protection from winter storms. (With permission of the West Sussex Library Service).

**Figure 59**

This view in 1935 provides another view of the low sea wall. Note the small quantity of shingle. The position of the boats suggests that they are above the high tide mark on that day. (With permission of the West Sussex Library Service).

**Figure 60**
This view in 1935 is east of the sea wall. The man in the foreground has just stepped over a wooden barricade, and he is about to step over a palisade made of sticks placed in trenches, a technique that was often used after World War II. There are several low groynes further along the beach. (With permission of the West Sussex Library Service).

**Figure 61**
Davenport Road in Felpham Beach Estate in the 1920s - 60 yards from the sea. (Postcard provided by the late Pat Esmonde-White).

## World War II

Looking back at the war, instead of secrecy there is now a vast amount of reliable information coming from both sides of the conflict. For instance, the Allies moved across Germany near the end of the war so rapidly that the bulk of the enemy's records were intact when they fell into their hands. One can now read in translation the various, developing views of the German leaders about the expected invasion of Britain.

## Local people

The British people living near the coast undoubtedly showed great courage when invasion seemed imminent. In 1940 they were advised that school children, mothers with young children, infirm people, and retired and elderly people should leave. A year later a poster was displayed in many coastal towns (Figure 62). In large letters, it ended:

**Figure 62
Poster in 1941.**

> **When invasion is upon us it may be necessary to evacuate the remaining population of this and certain other towns. Evacuation would then be compulsory at short notice, in crowded trains, with scanty luggage, to destinations chosen by the Government. If you are not among the essential workers mentioned above, it is better to go now while the going is good.**

Until the German invasion of the Low Countries, the greatest threat of invasion of England was in East Anglia and the South-East, but after the Germans occupied Normandy and Brittany the threat moved to the South Coast, with Felpham in a vulnerable position.

## Felpham Beach

Visitors and holiday-makers were strongly discouraged from going to the seaside. Certainly, nobody was allowed on the beach, and photography was absolutely forbidden.

The defence of the beach was the responsibility of a Division of the Canadian Army, which was mainly based on the South Downs so that units could move rapidly in any direction in an emergency. On the beach their engineers constructed anti-landing devices – 20 feet high and sloping landward (Figure 63), as well as concrete tank traps (Figure 64) to deter invasion. They also mined the area of wetlands later occupied by Butlin's.

I asked Jennifer Austin, who lived in Davenport Road during the war, about not being allowed on the beach. "Oh", she said, "we children simply climbed through the defences and played".

**Figure 63
Anti-landing devices**

**Figure 64
Tank traps.**

## War on the British Mainland

The war began in earnest within Britain when the Luftwaffe starting bombing aerodromes in England. Felpham was then in an area of considerable aerial activity, due largely to Tangmere and Ford Aerodromes nearby. Later, many enemy bombers dropped bombs as they flew along the coast and back.

In a Stuka raid on Tangmere on August 16th, 1940, 13 people were killed and many more were injured. Seven Hurricanes were destroyed and much of the base was wrecked. Without hesitation, Tangmere retaliated: it claimed 88 planes shot down, 29 probables and 39 damaged during the same month. Much more was to come. As well as acting as a fighter base, bombers used Tangmere for emergency landings and Lysanders delivered agents in France.

Ford Aerodrome was attacked by 13 to 15 dive bombers on August 18th, 1940. Fourteen people were killed and extensive damage was done to two hangers and other buildings.

## Local Defence Volunteers

The Local Defence Volunteers was formed in May 1940 and quickly renamed Home Guard at the request of Winston Churchill. In 1941, Leslie Garrett and his friend Gordon Bennett were 14-year-old Felpham sea scouts. They decided to lie about their ages and apply to join (Figure 65). As a result, Leslie spent many hours on lookout duty on St. Mary's Church Tower or manning a Vickers machine-gun - equipped with just one box of ammunition to face the German battalions! (Figure 66). Later, because the Regular Army could no longer be spared, he was transferred to 149 Coastal Battery, Royal Artillery, which was responsible for two 5.5" coastal guns in Aldwick, west of Bognor Regis. In 1943 Gordon joined the Royal Navy and Leslie, to his delight, joined the Royal Marines. When aged 17, he was a gunner on HMS Diadem, a light cruiser, during the landings on Juno and Sword Beaches in Normandy on D-Day. Leslie and Gordon were two of many local wartime heroes, over thirty of whom, sadly, sacrificed their lives.

**Figure 65**
**Leslie Garrett on his 15th birthday.**

## Dunkirk

At Dunkirk in June 1940, 338,000 troops were rescued: 103,000 in 56 destroyers, 87,000 in smaller vessels of the Royal Navy, 48,000 in 38 minesweepers, 5,000 in private motor boats, and 287 in trawlers and drifters. The troops had left behind: 7,000 tons of ammunition, 8,000 machine guns, 2,300 artillery pieces, 400 anti-tank guns, 90,000 rifles, and many motor vehicles.

Inevitably, our men were exhausted immediately after Dunkirk. At that stage they possessed only 50 infantry tanks, 100 cruiser tanks and 500 heavy guns to fend off an invasion. Mercifully, within two months they were reequipped with guns and ammunition from the United States – much of it heavily greased since World War I.

By comparison, the German Army had raced through the Low Countries, outflanked the Maginot Line and hurried on to Paris. They seemed invincible.

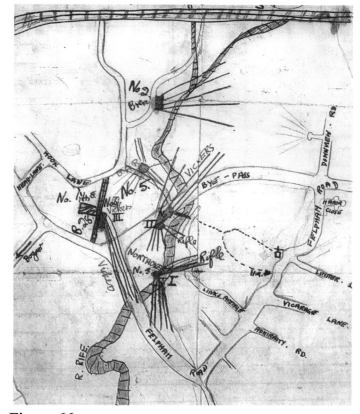

**Figure 66**
**The disposition of Home Guard defences at Felpham in 1941-2. (Thanks to Leslie Garrett).**

## German Plans

Before the war, in May 1939, Hitler wrote a Directive setting out German plans, *"If success comes in occupying Holland and Belgium, and also knocking out France, the basis for a successful war has been created against England".*

As early as a month after the war began, the Germans decided that, in order to wage air and sea warfare against England, it was first necessary to defeat the French and British armies and secure a firm base on part of the coast facing England.

## War in the air

The history of the Battle of Britain has been told too often to be repeated. Certainly, Germany's objective of destroying the RAF was not achieved.

**Figure 67**
**Hitler discussing plans for invasion.**

## War on the sea

At the beginning of the war, Admiral Raeder wrote: *"The surface forces are so inferior in number and strength to the British fleet that, even at full strength, they can do no more than show that they know how to die gallantly."*

In fact, the British Navy outnumbered the German Navy by ten to one. Then, in the Norwegian campaign, which began in April 1940, half of the German destroyers were sunk and some of their capital ships were disabled. Little wonder that Raeder never believed that an invasion of Britain could succeed. Soon afterwards he stipulated four tough provisos: 1. The enemy naval forces must either be eliminated or completely sealed off; 2. All threats to a landing fleet from enemy submarines must be eliminated; 3. The enemy air force must be completely destroyed; 4. Vessels for the invasion must be designed and manufactured.

In July 1940 the German generals demanded a surprise attack on a broad front, with an invasion from Ramsgate to Cornwall. To accommodate that demand, the German admirals' plans included an attack on the Portsmouth to Brighton sector setting out from Le Havre and involving 10 regiments, 25 steamers, 250 barges, 90 tugs and 180 motor-boats for that sector alone.

However, the Navy persisted in emphasising the transport problems, so the target was later changed to a frontage from Ramsgate to Worthing, and then from Folkestone to Brighton. Later still, a more detailed plan was to land 110,000 men and 24,000 horses in three days!

Whereas Napoleon had time to build landing craft designed for the purpose, Hitler could only improvise. After Dunkirk the obvious time to invade was in the following two months, but at that stage he was clearly not ready: he had only 45 converted river barges. Remarkably, the adapted barges were increased to over 2,000 by September, mostly from the Rhine. However, nearly all of them had little or no power, so they had to be towed by tugs and other small vessels – at 3 to 4 knots across the strong tidal currents in the English Channel. They would then have to repeat the journey at least twice. It would have been a very different story if Germany had the type of landing craft that were employed so successfully by the Allies later in the war.

The Germans used considerable ingenuity in tackling the problem of getting tanks ashore, including designing amphibian and submersible tanks. The latter had to be driven blind, with snorkels attached to buoys for air supply.

Maps are available to show where mines and U-boats would be located to prevent ships from Portsmouth leaving the Solent. Due south of Felpham, 750 sea mines and 1,000 explosive buoys were to be laid in two rows, 5.4 and 16.3 miles long. The U-boats in European waters were to be deployed in three groups: one in the North Sea, one between Cornwall and Brittany, and one at the exit from the East Solent. Perhaps that explains the presence today of two submarine wrecks due south of Felpham, and several others nearby.

In January 1943 a sea mine exploded on Felpham Beach opposite Davenport Road in Felpham Beach Estate. Two people were injured and approximately 150 houses were damaged, two seriously. A week later a second sea mine exploded less than a mile to the east, opposite Strand Way near Third Avenue in Summerley Estate, doing similar damage. At several other times during the war mines were seen offshore and towed to safety.

### What would have happened?

The Germans calculated that they must have a quarter-moon and a high tide two hours before dawn, and hence they knew the days in September 1940 that fulfilled those requirements. Of course, the British made the same calculations, so Churchill was informed when the invasion was likely to take place. Also, the Navy and the RAF followed carefully the activities on the French Coast. As a result, our Navy ships would have set out the day before the invasion. Five cruisers and 42 destroyers, from Plymouth, Portsmouth, Sheerness and Harwich, would be waiting offshore, while Germany had only 6 destroyers available. With British destroyers travelling at 36 knots and German tugs at 3 to 4 knots, it would have been a massacre. No Germans would have reached England alive.

On September 17th, 1940, Hitler accepted the inevitable: he abandoned his plans for an invasion of Britain and turned towards Russia.

### Bognor Regis, Felpham and the war in the air

During the war, 200 bombs and mines were dropped on Bognor Regis, and a few on Felpham.

In the Bognor area, 37 aircraft crashed, including four in Felpham - one offshore, one on the foreshore and one near Sea Road. In April 1942 a Hampden bomber, returning from a raid on Dortmund, crashed in a field near the south end of Sea Road. Local residents attempted to help despite the flames, not knowing that there were four unexploded bombs on board. The four airman who died are remembered by a memorial plaque near the scene (Figure 68).

**Figure 68**
**Memorial plaque**

### D-day

Before D-day there were Allied troops everywhere within several miles of Portsmouth. The 3rd Battalion 120th Infantry Regiment and the 30th US Infantry Division were billeted at Felpham, and eventually the entire Eastern Task Force was assembled in the Solent.

The Invasion Fleet was the largest, best planned, best trained and best equipped ever (Figure 69).

**Figure 69**
**D-Day Invasion Fleet. (A photograph by Frank L'Allouette).**

## After the war

When the Army had removed all the wartime obstacles it was obvious that the neglect and damage to the coastal defences would lead to still more damage. Furthermore, no money was available to construct major new defences. Photographs in 1945 of the groynes and sea wall at nearby Bognor Regis illustrate the problem (Figures 70 and 71).

**Figure 70**
   **Groynes in 1945. (With permission of the West Sussex Record Office).**

**Figure 71**
   **Sea wall in 1945. (With permission of the West Sussex Record Office).**

**Figure 72**
   **Groynes on Felpham Beach in 1948.**

**Figure 73**
   **The zig-zag defence.**

**Figure 74**
   **A layer of concrete.**

The coastal defences of much of Felpham Beach were still the responsibility of the landowners as a relic of the past. For instance, when the 'estate man' on Felpham Beach Estate was appointed in the late 1940s, it was stipulated that he would spend half of each week attempting to maintain the defences on the beach (Figure 72).

Only later did all the coastal defence become the responsibility of the Bognor Regis Urban District Council. Some groynes were repaired, then a zig-zag defence was constructed (Figure 73), a palisade of sticks in a trench was placed in front of it, and hardcore was used to fill the spaces behind the zig-zag defence. Figure 74 shows a layer of concrete in front of 28 Davenport Road. In the distance the concrete gives way to an informal path, with vegetation between the path and the sea. By then the zig-zag defence and the wooden steps were almost buried in shingle.

Then came disaster (Figure 75). The sea thrust aside the feeble defences and started to erode some gardens in Davenport Road.

**Figure 75**
   **Disaster at Felpham. Note the poor protection by the largely destroyed groynes and the inadequate palisade of sticks.**

## Lewis and Duvivier

Fortunately, the Borough Council consulted Lewis and Duvivier, probably the best firm of coastal engineers in the country. It was led by J Duvivier, who knew more about the West Sussex coastal defences than anyone. In 1962 he wrote:

 ' ... *the prevailing alongshore movement of beach shingle is eastwards towards Middleton and Littlehampton. The shingle was derived originally from the erosion of the gravel beds in the cliffs in the vicinity of Selsey Bill.*

*In the course of its eastward travel large masses of shingle have come to rest temporarily at Pagham Harbour, where the drift has been intercepted temporarily by harbour works and groynes. The drift has also been intercepted by groynes on the Aldwick frontage, on the Bognor town frontage and on the River Board frontage east of the town. Only the shingle which has managed to find its way past these obstructions has come to rest temporarily on the Felpham frontage before flowing on towards Middleton.*

*The quantity of shingle moving towards Bognor has been diminishing year by year as more and more of the coast to the west has been groyned. For example, since the River Board built their new sea wall and rebuilt the groynes on their frontage just east of the town, hardly any shingle has been by-passing the River Board's terminal groyne at Outram Road.*

*The present shortage of shingle will not improve with the passage of time; in fact the situation will deteriorate because the principal source of supply, namely the cliffs of Selsey Bill, have been sealed off against further erosion by the recently completed Selsey Coast Protection Scheme'.*

In 1965 Lewis and Duvivier drew the plans of the defences that were to be constructed in 1965/7. They still constitute the basic features of our current defences (Figures 76 and 77).

However, four years before that there was a problem: the Borough Engineer correctly insisted on access to the beach for heavy vehicles so that repairs and other essential procedures could be carried out. So, in order to construct a promenade/roadway, the Council attempted to compulsorily purchase parts of several properties under the Coastal Protection Act, while the residents held that the Act permitted the building of the sea wall but not the acquisition of their land. Making legal history, this case ended in the High Court, where the decision was in favour of the residents and the Council was blamed for any delay that had

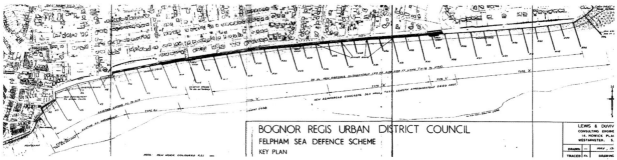

**Figure 76**
**Lewis and Duvivier Plan, illustrating the new groynes.**

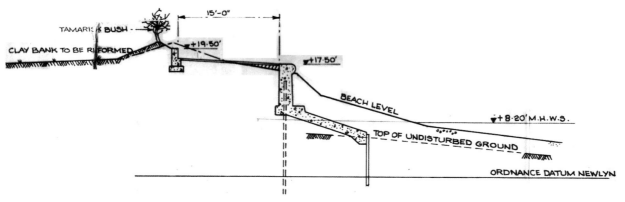

**Figure 77**
**A representative cross-section of the Lewis and Duvivier Wall.**

occurred. Then there was a compromise: the home-owners agreed to the promenade being built provided they retained ownership of their land. This had some strange consequences.

The Lewis and Duvivier defences were completed in 1965-7 (Figures 76 and 77). Shortly afterwards two adjoining home-owners in Davenport Road had a tall wire fence erected around their properties on the promenade. For several years we had to tip-toe outside the cage in a space about 4-foot wide that belonged to the Council.

Overall the Lewis and Duvivier plan was a considerable achievement. In addition to its

**Figure 78**
**The Lewis and Duvivier Promenade.**

serious role in coastal defence, the promenade became a welcome social success. For example, people now travel long distances at weekends to walk along the promenade and back (Figure 78).

**New coastal defence problems**
In the summer of 1992 the residents of Felpham were taken by surprise: we learned that Arun District Council was consulting the public about five schemes designed by a different company of coastal engineers. First, there was a circular distributed to all relevant organisations in Felpham, and then a public exhibition of the Options. In response, at a meeting of the Felpham Beach Householders Association in 1992, I was invited to form a committee to assess the issues involved.

**Felpham Sea Defence Committee**
The Sea Defence Committee was created gradually. Eventually there were representatives of almost all districts from Selsey to Littlehampton and most relevant organisations in Felpham and Bognor Regis, including the Felpham Parish Council, the five districts most directly affected - Felpham Beach Estate, Summerley Estate, Summerley II, Culver Road, and the Snook's Corner Community (which together represent several hundred households), Felpham Sailing Club, Felpham Trader's Association, Felpham Village Conservation Society, the Women's Institute, Bognor Environment and Amenities Movement, Felpham Ratepayers Association, Littlehampton Civic Society and the Felpham Parochial Church Council. As I wrote in the Preface, the members included: a research engineer specialising in fluid dynamics, a civil engineer who had been involved in building the Thames Barrier, a marine biologist, two scientists experienced in research, a quantity surveyor, a former harbourmaster/ship's pilot at Littlehampton, a coastal defence contractor, a subaqua diver/archaeologist/geologist with unrivalled experience of our coastline, an estate agent, a few politicians, sailors and a banker. We also consulted local fishermen and shopkeepers. In all, the committee conducted almost fifty formal meetings that were attended with great enthusiasm.

In 1993 our committee organised a series of six scientific meetings at Bognor Town Hall at which up to a hundred local people from the Witterings to Brighton discussed important issues concerning the coastal defence of West Sussex with some of the country's leading experts. These meetings provided us with further invaluable contacts and sources of information, not only among local enthusiasts and experts but also at Portsmouth and Southampton Universities and at Hydraulics Research. In 1995 we organised a further six meetings.

At the outset we made our own observations on the beach and confirmed that several worrying problems had arisen. Obviously something had to be done, but what?

**Figure 79**
Loss of shingle.

**Figure 80**
The garden of 10 Davenport Road after a storm.

**Figure 81**
Storm waves from the south-east.

## The prolems
### Loss of shingle and storm waves

Unfortunately, much of our shingle had been lost (Figure 79). It is undoubtedly our most valuable natural defence as it absorbs the energy of the waves. Consequently its retention is an essential element when planning coastal defence on the South Coast. As a result, storm waves struck the sea wall with such force that sea water and shingle were thrown high into the air, and the houses near the sea shook with each wave. Several properties were regularly flooded, and some residents found shingle in their gardens (Figure 80).

In recent years, storms have become more frequent. They are also often from the south or south-east, instead of the usual south-west, resulting in more damaging waves. Figure 81 shows a threatening wave from the south-east.

### Flood risk

The most vulnerable part of our coastline is the indentation where the White Mill was lost.

Figure 82 is the first consultant's map of the part of Felpham most at risk of flooding. However, this misses two important points, possibly because the consultant was mainly interested in showing sufficient property loss to justify his plans for coastal defence.

The first point is that the whole of the area of the ancient waterway, all 3 1/2 square miles, would be at risk, including much of the rest of Felpham village, Butlin's, Tesco's, the industrial area at Shripney, the A29 and the railway, which might all be flooded. Unmitigated disaster!

The second point is important: the risk does not depend on the level only, but also on the ability of the flood water to escape. As I wrote on page 28, water in the middle of Felpham Beach Estate would run away towards Limmer Lane. In contrast, water in the Butlin's or Sea Road areas could not escape because of the promenade and the sea wall.

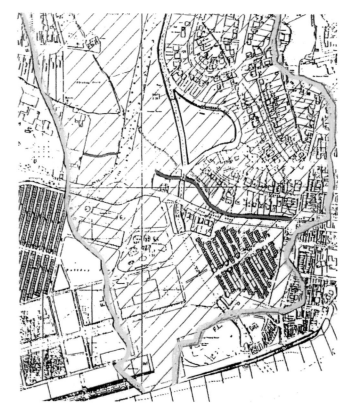

**Figure 82**
**The first consultant's flood map. (The limits of the area most at risk are marked in yellow and the 15th century earthworks in red).**

**Figure 83**
**Crack in the sea wall.**

### Sand loss

Due principally to the shingle loss, unimpeded waves bounced off the wall and repeatedly carried sand from the beach out to sea, particularly in winter.

Deterioration in the sea wall

Inevitably, the sea wall had deteriorated during nearly 30 years of assault by storm waves. In several places the apron of the wall (the sloping section at the base) was visible (Figure 79). In a few sections the metal sheeting below the apron was also exposed (see Figure 77). And a few cracks had appeared (Figure 83).

Also, in the 30 years since the Lewis and Duvivier defences the sea had risen several inches and the tide had moved further towards the land.

**The Options**

Four of the five Options proposed by Arun District Council in the summer of 1992 are shown in Figures 84 to 87.

Option 1   Costing £7.9 to 8.9 million, this Option consisted of 110,000 tonnes of rock built into 16 large rock groynes, with 589,000 cubic metres of beach recharge. After consultation, this Option was chosen by Arun District Council Option as the most suitable – but not by the Environment Agency, which was responsible for the coastline from Gloucester Road to Outram Road, in other words in front of the old waterway.

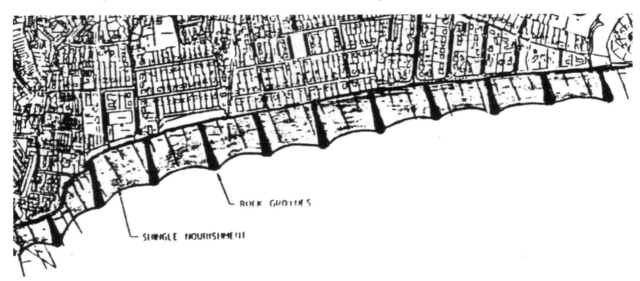

**Figure 84**
**Option 1.**

**Figure 85**
**Option 2.**

Option 2    Costing £6.8 million, this was the most straight-forward and shocking Option: simply eliminating Felpham Beach would save the cost of maintenance! 210,000 tonnes of rock were to be imported by sea to build a rock revetment (rock wall) near Low Water, about 150 yards from the sea wall. The beach would then be covered by 250,000 cubic metres of rubble. The surface had not been agreed but it seemed likely to be the equivalent of porous tarmac. Local residents asked if the area might then be used as a car park!

Option 3    Costing £14.7 million, this Option consisted mainly of offshore breakwaters like those at Elmer and 718,000 cubic metres of shingle.

Option 4    Costing £21.1 million, this Option would be comprised mainly of two large headlands built of 350,000 tonnes of rock.

**Figure 86**
  **Option 3**

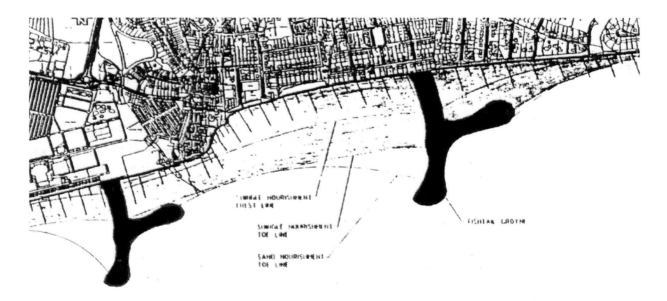

**Figure 87**
  **Option 4.**

**Further consultants**

Fortunately for us, in the summer of 1993 we learned that a highly respected company of coastal engineers had been employed to review the five Options independently. We and the Felpham Parish Council were not allowed to read their report, but it resulted in all five Options being abandoned and the appointment of a third company. To our regret, as time was short the new company had to adopt much of the fundamental data on which the very unsatisfactory original Options had been based.

In January 1994 we were sent copies of the first company's Final Report and the contract for the new consulting engineers shortly to be appointed. Both documents caused us grave concern. Briefly, the Final Report confirmed our worst fears. In our opinion it was short of appropriate research and fundamental information, and unjustified in some of its conclusions. The five Options were apparently buried, but the data on which they were based lived on.

Early in 1994, a third company was appointed. Within a few weeks, three tentative schemes were shown to the public, and then a preferred scheme was presented to the Key Consultees, including the Felpham Sea Defence Committee, on May 28th, 1994 (Figures 88 to 90).

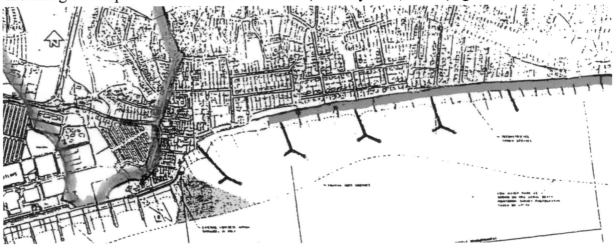

**Figure 88**
**The Preferred Option. I have coloured in green the limits of the area most at risk of flooding shown in Figure 81 in green. The SSS1, Site of Special Scientific Interest, is the yellow area in the sea. The red area, which is the area least at risk, is where most of the structure would be built. Massive, long fishtail rock groynes are also shown.**

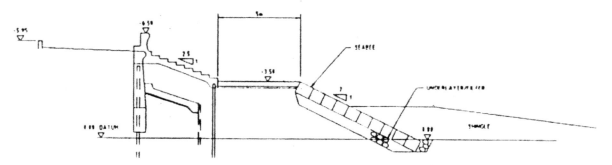

**Figure 89**
**Cross-section of the Preferred Option .**

Figure 88 illustrates that the indentation where the White Windmill was lost, which we regarded as particularly vulnerable, was apparently to have the least protection. Also, the proposal to construct fish-tail rock groynes extending among our natural rocks was a cause of great concern and forced us to intensify our campaign.

52

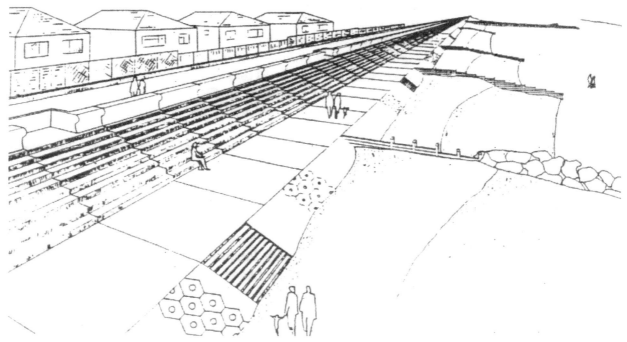

**Figure 90**
**The main section of the Preferred Option.**

Naturally, we were alarmed by the massive 'sea wall'. In June 1994, we wrote to all concerned giving our opinion of this item:

*"Apart from being very expensive, unsuitable for a coastal village, and in the wrong place to prevent major flooding, we believe that the design drawings of the sea wall contain some fundamental errors:*

*1. The shingle level shown is 2.75 metres too low. It should be half-way up the continuous steps, well above the couple walking with a dog.*

*2. The timber groynes are at least a metre too low, and they are well away from the original wall so that the lower promenade would provide the shingle with an unimpeded path eastwards.*

*3. The whole structure has an overall gradient of 1 in 3, so that storm waves and shingle would be projected towards the neighbouring property instead of upwards, which would increase flooding and damage to property*

*4. The SEABEE system (shown as hexagonals) would soon be choked by shingle".*

Our strong objections to that scheme were the subjects of a prolonged publicity campaign and extensive consultation. Then came the formal Environmental Assessment of the scheme, which had little impact. Despite our efforts, the scheme remained Arun's widely proclaimed Preferred Option for seven months, from June 1994 until January 1995.

**Posford Duvivier**

At that stage I sought help from Brian Waters at Posford Duvivier, the successor to Lewis and Duvivier, who had built our sea wall in 1965/7. Brian had vast experience of coastal engineering on the West Sussex coast. Starting work with Lewis and Duvivier as a site junior in 1956, he had worked on site during the construction of our own sea wall in 1965/7.

Brian was very generous: he visited Felpham three times and spent an evening with our Sea Defence Committee. As an extra courtesy, I was shown around the latest developments at headquarters. Later, two other engineers from Posford and Duvivier visited Felpham and one of them sketched what we needed in the form of three drawings.

## Hydraulics Research

At the end of 1994 the Preferred Option was subjected to extensive wave basin modelling at Hydraulics Research near Oxford, which we were invited to witness. Probably as a result of their Interim Report, the Preferred Option was then stated by Arun District Council to be unlikely to be accepted. Instead, it was insisted that anyone with other plans must make them available for testing at Hydraulics Research as time was short. At first the engineers at Posford Duvivier vigorously opposed the request, but they obliged when contacted directly by Arun District Council, who then arranged for their scheme to be tested at Hydraulics Research.

In September 1995 we had access to the Final Report on the Preferred Option written by Hydraulics Research. We found much to accept and some things to criticise. For instance, we welcomed:

1. *"The limited effectiveness of the landward ends of the groynes was particularly noticeable on the eastern frontage where shingle was swept unhindered along the berm ... ";*

2. *".. the discharges measured during the 10 and 100 year events in particular were still sufficient to pose a danger to pedestrians and vehicular traffic whilst also being liable to cause structural damage to buildings sited immediately landward of the sea wall";*

3. *"Shingle almost totally filled the voids of any SEABEE units ... ".*

To our surprise, seaweed had been modelled by using plastic balls on the surface of the water. Despite the waves, these balls never reached the shore, conclusively invalidating the experiment. We concluded that they were testing the wrong kind of seaweed, apparently because of previous studies of kelp in Worthing. Our 'slub' travels on the seabed and certainly reaches the shore!

## Further consultation

In January 1995, I was invited to an important meeting with engineers from Arun District Council, from the current consultant company, and from Posford Duvivier. At that meeting the engineers from Posford Duvivier explained more fully what they had in mind. Although the current consultants did not accept that their proposals were necessary, there followed a major revision of their original scheme during the later stages of modelling.

At a public meeting soon afterwards, a radical change in policy was announced. After analysing, debating and rejecting ten Options, we were then presented with a simple plan that was estimated to cost just under £3 million - down from the maximum of over £21 million. At last there was a scheme that we could all accept. After five years in which we were treated as the enemy, we suddenly took on the role of well-informed allies. From then on there was maximum co-operation and we were consulted at every stage. For instance, we were able to negotiate modifications of the plan to suit the needs of the local yachtsmen and fishermen. Later, during construction in 1999, three of us were invited to attend 3-weekly site visits and to make suggestions on behalf of the local people, and those suggestions were always accepted.

## Principles of the final plan

1. The scheme would provide suitable protection throughout the length of the Arun frontage.

2. The rock groynes (Figure 88) were abandoned. Instead the timber groynes were to be rebuilt and heightened near the sea wall to accommodate the expected sea rise in the coming century.

3. The massive sea wall was withdrawn (Figures 88 to 90). Instead the existing sea wall was to be repaired, and a larger bullnose added.

4. The promenade was to be repaired and resurfaced.

5. The rear wave wall was to remain at the same height.

6. Special ramps were designed for the Felpham Yacht Club, for the fishermen, and for launching boats.

7. Large rocks, imported from Norway, were to be positioned to stabilise the shingle near the sea wall, the ramps and some groynes (Figure 91 and Preface).

8. Massive quantities of pebbles, grit and sand were to be conveyed by a large tube from a ship offshore in order to recharge the beach (Figure 92).

**Figure 91**
Rocks from Norway.

**Figure 92**
Beach recharge – pebbles, grit and sand delivered by a pipe from the ship in the distance.

## Twenty-first century

The engineers who designed our 1998/9 coastal defence project, and the engineers who carried out the work, had every reason to be proud of their achievements.

Vulnerable areas of Felpham have been protected from flooding. Before 1999 houses near the sea shuddered with every storm wave, and sea water and shingle were thrown high into the air. Since the defence work most of the energy of the waves has been absorbed by the shingle (Figure 93) and sand has increased as waves no longer rebound from the seawall.

Apart from the technical success, our own greatest pleasure has been that we helped to prevent schemes that would have ruined Felpham Beach. Of course, we understand that more drastic measures will be essential in years to come.

**Figure 93**
**The shingle in 2009.**

## Pastimes

It would be easy to write other books about the alterations in pastimes and beachware over the last century. For example, bikinis are now worn. Wetsuits, which have transformed the entire British coast, often protect both adults and children. Swimming, paddling and rock-pooling are as popular as ever.

Many people regularly walk along the tranquil beach near low tide, often with their dogs (see Front Cover). Some amble along the promenade, others just sit and look, while others prefer coffee or ice cream (Figures 94 and 95).

The beach huts are now more formal and have been moved back from the sea (Figure 96).The putting green and tennis courts are also popular (Figure 97), and amateur fishing regularly attracts enthusiasts.

Felpham Yacht Club was opened in 1958 and has been a great success (Figures 1, 98 and 100). In addition to sailing, surfing and kite-surfing are now very popular.

The Royal National Lifeboat Institution stages a demonstration opposite Felpham Beach every summer (Figure 99).

And so on.

**Figure 94**
   **The Lobster Pot, built a few yards inland from where the White Mill was destroyed by the sea.**

**Figure 95**
   **The Boat House, built on the site of the Coastguard Boat House.**

**Figure 96**
**Bathing huts.**

**Figure 97**
**Tennis courts and putting green.**

**Figure 98**
**Felpham Sailing Club.**

**Figure 99**
**The Royal National Lifeboat Institution annual demonstration opposite Felpham Beach.**

## Postscripts

After the beach had settled down following the coastal defence works in 1999, I received a gracious letter from a senior executive at Arun District Council, who was not personally involved in the negotiations. He wrote,

*"Arun's officers (including me) have learnt important lessons over the past five years, in particular the importance of real, rather than token, dialogue with community groups".*

One of the nicest compliments about the beach that we received came from a lady who said:

*"I don't know what the fuss was about. It looks exactly as it did before."*

**Figure 100**
**Launching for an international regatta opposite Felpham Sailing Club.**

# Index

# Souces and suggested reading

1. Ballard, A, 1910. The Sussex Coast Line. *Sussex Archaeol. Collections.* LIII: 5-25.

2. Bewley, R, 1994. *Prehistoric Settlements.* London: Batsford.

3 Binnie and Partners, 1987. *Report on Seaweed at Worthing.*

4. Bone, D, 1986. The Stratigraphy of the Reading Beds (Palaeocene) at Felpham, West Sussex'. *Tertiary Research.* 8: 17-29.

5. Brewerton, D (ed), 1993. *Coastal Defence: Selsey to Brighton.*

6. Brewerton, D (ed), 1995. *The Future of West Sussex: Coastal Defence, Selsey to Brighton.*

7. Crook, P, 1998. *Sussex Home Guard.* Midhurst: Middleton Press.

8. Dickinson, C, 1963. *British Seaweeds.* London: Eyre and Spottiswoode.

9. Felpham and Middleton Local History Workshop, 1995, *The Incoming Tide.*

10. Felpham and Middleton Local History Workshop, 2010. *Sea, Ships and Smugglers.*

11. Felpham and Middleton Local History Workshop, 2010. *Swallowed by the Sea.*

12. Felpham and Middleton Local History Workshop, 2008. *20th Century War Memorials in Felpham and Middleton.*

13. Franklin, A and Philp, M, 2003. *Napoleon and the Invasion of Britain.* Bodleian Library.

14. Gilchrist, A, 1863. *Life and Works of William Blake.* London: Macmillan.

15. Goodwin, J, 1985. *The Military Defence of West Sussex.* Midhurst: Middleton Press.

16. Gould, S, 1996. *Felpham Matters.* Emsworth: Westbrook Press.

17. Gupta, S, Collier, J et al., 2007. Catastrophic flooding origin of shelf valley systems in the English Channel. *Nature.* 448: 342-5.

18. Hamblin, R et al. 1992. *British Geological Survey: The geology of the English Channel.* London: HMSO.

19. Hanson, N, 2003. *The Confident Hope of a Miracle The True History of the Spanish Armada.* London: Corgi Books.

20. Harrington, P, 2007. *The Castles of Henry VIII.* Botley, Oxford, Osprey Publishing.

21. G A Kellaway, G A et al., 1975. The Quarternary History of the English Channel. *Phil. Trans. R. Soc. London.* 279: 189-218.

22. Duvivier, J, 1962. *'Proof of Evidence: Bognor Urban District Council Coast Protection Act 1949 Felpham Works Scheme'.*

23. Martin, E C, 1932. 'Chalk Zones in the Foreshore between Worthing and Felpham, Sussex' *Proc. Geologists Assoc. London.* 43: 201-211.

24. McKie, R, 2006. *Face of Britain.* London: Simon and Schuster.

25. L G Mouchel and Partners, 1995. *'Environmental Statement: Proposed Coastal Defence Scheme, Felpham, West Sussex'.*

26. Nottage, A S, 1995. *Summary of Seaweed Study.* H R Wallingford.

27. Parish, W, 1835. 'Notice of Fossils found in the Bognor Rocks'. *Trans. Geological Society.* V: 262.

28. Philippe, M, 1995. *History of Two Empires.* Napoleonica la Revue.

29. Pryor, F, 1998. *Farmers in Prehistoric Britain.* Port Stroud (Glos.): Tempus.

30. Raine, K, 1970. *William Blake.* Oxford University Press.

31. Robinson, D, 2005. *Invasion, 1940: 'The Truth about the Battle of Britain and What Stopped Hitler.* New York: Carroll and Graf.

32. Saunders, A. 1995. *Bognor at War.* Midhurst: Middleton Press.

33. Sykes, B, 2007. *Saxons, Vikings, and Celts.* New York: Norton.

34. Wallace, H, 1990. *Sea level and Shoreline between Portsmouth and Pagham for the past 2500 years.*

35. H R Wallingford, 1995. *Report on Work Commissioned by Arun District Council on behalf of both ADC and the National Rivers Authority Southern Region'.*

36. Waugh, M, 1985. *Smuggling in Kent and Sussex. 1700-1840.* Newbury: Countryside Books.

37. Robert West and Partners, 1993. *Arun District Council and National Rivers Authority Joint Coastal Defence Scheme, Felpham, West Sussex - Summary Report'.*

38. Wikipedia. *Caesar's Invasions of Britain.*

39. Wikipedia. *Napoleon 1 of France.*

40. Wikipedia. *William 1 of England.*

41. Williamson, J, 1961. *The Englsh Channel.* London, Collins.

42. www. british-history online, 1997. *A History of the County of Sussex: Felpham .*

43. www.raf.mod.uk/bob1940: *Battle of Britain Campaign Diary.*

44. Wymer, N, 1972. *Companion into Sussex.* Bourne End: Spurbooks.

45 Venables, E M, 1931. Notes on the Geology of Felpham, near Bognor Regis. *Proc. Geologists Assoc. London.* 42: 362-369.